Little Bear's
Christmas

Little Bear's Christmas

Norbert Landa

Illustrated by

Marlis Scharff-Kniemeyer

TED SMART

It was autumn in Bear Valley. The wind ripped the bright leaves from the trees and swept them into great rustling heaps.

'I can do something you can't do!' shouted Bertie Bear gleefully. He scrambled up a tree and then let himself drop into the soft pile of leaves below.

Wolfie Wolf and Wilfred Wolf watched him.

'Autumn leaves are the best!' shouted Bertie.

'Huh!' snorted Wolfie. 'Winter snow is better.'

'Snow?' wondered Bertie. He had never heard of snow before.

'That's because you bears sleep through the winter,' said Wilfred.

'Nonsense,' growled Bertie. 'You're just jealous because you can't climb trees.'

The next day the three friends went out to fly their kites. Bertie's kite flew the highest.

'Flying kites may be fun,' said Wolfie grumpily, 'but Father Christmas is better. He brings lovely presents and we all sing Christmas carols.'

'Sing?' laughed Bertie. 'The way you wolves howl, I'd rather be asleep!'

The following morning Bertie, Wolfie and Wilfred went to gather mushrooms.

'Look, there! And here! And here!' called Bertie. 'See how many mushrooms I've found already. We'll have a delicious supper tonight.'

Wolfie and Wilfred looked glumly into their empty baskets.

'Mushrooms are yummy!' said Wilfred.

'Maybe. But honey cakes and chocolate hearts from Father Christmas are best,' said Wolfie.

That evening Bertie asked his mother to tell him all about winter, the snow and Father Christmas.

'Winter is very cold and bleak,' said Mrs Bear. 'The mushrooms and berries disappear, and even the rain freezes. It turns white and settles on the ground, and people call it snow. Sensible people, like us bears, go to bed and stay there until the warm spring arrives.'

'And what about Father Christmas?' asked Bertie.

'I was coming to him,' said Mrs Bear. 'People who don't sleep through the winter aren't as lucky as we are. They have to trudge about in the cold snow. Father Christmas gives them something to look forward to in the dark days of winter.'

'What does he look like?'

'Well, I've never seen him, but people say he wears a red coat and has a white beard.'

Mrs Bear gave Bertie a big hug and sang him a lullaby.

'I suppose we bears do have to sleep through Christmas,' thought Bertie afterwards, 'but I so want to see Father Christmas. I think I know how to, as well. If I try to sleep as much as I can now, I'll be wide awake for Christmas!'

The next morning Bear Valley was shrouded in fog. Then it started to rain. Wolfie and Wilfred sailed their boats in the puddles, but Bertie stayed in bed.

'What's the matter?' asked Mrs Bear. 'Aren't you feeling well?'

'No, I'm fine,' said Bertie. 'I just want to sleep a little longer.'

'Sleep? At this time of day?' Mrs Bear was worried and called Dr Wolf.

Dr Wolf checked Bertie's tongue and took his temperature.

'This little one's fine,' he said. 'Perhaps the weather is making him tired. I can feel snow coming. I'm sure he'll be bright as a button by Christmas.'

Christmas? Bertie listened hard.

'Shhh, Doctor,' whispered Mrs Bear. 'Remember, we bears sleep through the winter.'

'Of course you do,' said the doctor. 'Well, sleep soundly.'

Dr Wolf hurried home. It was growing very cold, and dark clouds hung over Bear Valley. Snow was on its way.

A few days later Mrs Bear prepared the cottage for their winter sleep. She tied thick ropes around a sack of grain and hung it from the ceiling to keep it safe from the greedy mice. Then Mrs Bear locked the door, closed the shutters, and yawned.

'Time for bed,' she said, giving Bertie a good night kiss. 'Sleep well, little cub, until springtime.' Mrs Bear went into her bedroom, but came out again almost immediately. 'Have you seen my alarm clock?' she asked. Bertie lay as still as he could.

'Goodness, he's fast asleep already!' said Mrs Bear to herself. 'Never mind. I don't need an alarm clock. The spring sunshine will wake us up.' She tiptoed out of the room.

Bertie giggled quietly. 'I've hidden the alarm clock under my bed! It'll wake me up at Christmas – and then . . .' Bertie fell asleep.

In the valley the snow began to fall in thick, white flakes. The air was still. It was very peaceful. Inside the cottage the little bear slept for a very long time.

Suddenly the alarm clock shrilled. Bertie nearly fell out of bed with surprise. What a noise! He turned it off hurriedly. Had Mrs Bear heard it too? No, all Bertie could hear was Mrs Bear's gentle snoring. He threw open the shutters and looked out.

What a miracle! Someone had covered the whole of the valley with a white, fluffy blanket, as thick and soft as a featherbed. So this was snow! And, thought Bertie, where there's snow, Father Christmas can't be far away.

Bertie tied on his scarf, opened the door and stepped out into the shining white snow. He listened. He couldn't hear a sound.

'I'm going to find Father Christmas!' whispered Bertie and plodded up the hill. Every step left a small, deep paw-print. The snow felt fluffy, but it wasn't as warm as a featherbed. In fact, it was very cold. Amazing!

At last the little bear reached the top of the hill. From here he could see across the whole valley. Bertie looked in all directions. Where was Father Christmas?

Then he felt something cold and wet on his nose. A snowflake! And another one! Snowflakes came dancing down from the sky and Bertie danced with them until he was dizzy.

By the time Bertie stopped for breath there were so many whirling snowflakes that he could hardly see past his nose.

'Father Christmas, where are you?' he shouted. 'Can you hear me?'

But Father Christmas didn't answer.

Everything was silent.

The snow continued to flutter down from the sky. Bertie waited. His feet were getting cold. Then he began to feel hungry. And soon he started to feel frightened. Darkness was falling.

'How can I find Father Christmas in the dark?' sighed Bertie. 'I'd better go home while I can still find my way.'

The little bear slid down the hill, following the paw-prints he had left before. But the snow fell thickly and soon his paw-prints were covered over. Now Bertie didn't know where he was, or how to find his way home.

'Help!' shouted Bertie. 'I want to go home!'

Bertie strained his ears to catch any
sound. He could hear nothing
except a distant howling. Could that
be Wolfie and Wilfred singing? No,
it was only the wind. But then Bertie
heard a faint tinkling and a sleigh
appeared through the snowflakes.

'Hey! Stop!' shouted the little bear.
'Please, wait for me!'

The driver pulled on his reins and
turned round. He was wrapped from
head to toe in a thick blanket and
Bertie could see only a friendly face
with twinkling blue eyes. The little
bear stepped nearer and stared,
astonished. The sleigh had no
wheels! It sped across the snow on
huge skis, pulled by reindeer with
magnificent antlers.

'Hallo, Bertie!' cried the driver.
'Where have you come from?
Shouldn't little bears be asleep now?'

'Well, yes, they should really,'
murmured Bertie, embarrassed, 'but
I wanted to find Father Christmas,
and now I can't find my way home!'

'I thought so,' laughed the driver.
'Come with me - and hold tight!'

Bertie climbed aboard, amazed. 'Giddy up!' shouted the driver, and the reindeer gave a mighty leap. In no time the sleigh was flying through the air. Bertie was scared. The valley floor seemed so far below them. 'Hey! Where are we going?' he called out nervously.

'We're taking you home, of course!'

In no time the sleigh swept back to earth and landed right in front of the cottage. The driver leapt down from his seat and threw off the blanket. Now Bertie could see that he was wearing a red coat!

'Y-y-you're Father Christmas...' stammered the little bear.

'Of course I am,' whispered Father Christmas. 'But quiet now or you'll wake up your mother.' Father Christmas pulled the cloth off the sleigh and Bertie saw a huge heap of packets and parcels and presents.

'Now, what would you like for Christmas?' asked Father Christmas.

Bertie thought hard. 'I'll have - honey cakes and chocolate hearts. And for Mummy ... chocolate hearts and honey cakes!'

'Good,' said Father Christmas. He rummaged about in the sleigh and at last pulled out two squashy parcels. Together they carried the presents to the bears' cottage.

'I must go now,' whispered
Father Christmas.

'Wolfie and Wilfred are waiting
for me. And I'll tell you what, next Christmas
I'll bring you presents – but only if you're asleep,
all right?'

'All right,' agreed Bertie.

He watched as Father Christmas scrambled back up into the driver's seat. Then the sleigh shot off so fast that it sent sparks flying. Soon he could only see it as a tiny speck in the dark sky. Or was that a star? Bertie was much too tired to think about it now. He tiptoed into his room, hid the parcels in his toy chest and crawled into bed.

Then he slept.

When Bertie woke up it was daylight. He could smell flowers. Birds were twittering. Mrs Bear had thrown open the windows.

'Good morning, little one!' cried Mrs Bear, kissing Bertie on the nose. 'Time to get up! It's springtime!'

Springtime? Bertie rubbed his eyes and yawned. Then he remembered. 'Father Christmas was here!'

'The mice were here, you mean,' called Mrs Bear from the kitchen. 'Look what they've done to our sack of grain. They've chewed through the ropes and have eaten every scrap! What will we have for breakfast?'

'Honey cakes and chocolate hearts!' shouted Bertie, running to his toy box. 'And chocolate hearts and honey cakes!' Then he told Mrs Bear the whole story.

'And the best thing is - Father Christmas will come again next year!' finished the little bear.

'Yes,' agreed Mrs Bear, 'but only if you're asleep!'

A little later Wolfie and Wilfred peeped through the windows.
They sniffed the air curiously.

'That's funny!' they said. 'Your house smells all Christmassy!'

Mrs Bear and Bertie winked at one another. 'We bears
always celebrate Christmas a little late,' they said.
'Didn't you know?'

First published in Great Britain 1997
This edition produced for The Book People Ltd 1998
Hall Wood Avenue, Haydock, St Helens WA11 9UL

A CIP Catalogue record for this book is available from the British Library

First published 1997 by Ravensburger Buchverlag as Wo bist du, Weihnachtsmann?
Copyright © Ravensburger Buchverlag
Illustrations by Marlis Scharff-Kniemeyer
Text by Norbert Landa
English translation by Anna Trenter

ISBN 1 85613 490 3

10 9 8 7 6 5 4 3 2 1

Printed in Germany

Herbs

TIME
LIFE
BOOKS

THE GOOD COOK

WORLD WAR II

THE TIME-LIFE ENCYCLOPAEDIA
OF GARDENING

HUMAN BEHAVIOUR

THE GREAT CITIES

THE ART OF SEWING

THE OLD WEST

THE WORLD'S WILD PLACES

THE EMERGENCE OF MAN

LIFE LIBRARY OF PHOTOGRAPHY

TIME-LIFE LIBRARY OF ART

FOODS OF THE WORLD

GREAT AGES OF MAN

LIFE SCIENCE LIBRARY

LIFE NATURE LIBRARY

YOUNG READERS LIBRARY

THE TIME-LIFE ENCYCLOPAEDIA OF GARDENING

Herbs

by

James Underwood Crockett,

Ogden Tanner

and

the Editors of TIME-LIFE BOOKS

Watercolour Illustrations by

Richard Crist

TIME-LIFE INTERNATIONAL (NEDERLAND) B.V.

THE TIME-LIFE ENCYCLOPAEDIA
OF GARDENING

EDITORIAL STAFF FOR HERBS:

EDITOR: Robert M. Jones
Text Editor: Betsy Frankel
Picture Editor: Jean Tennant
Designer: Albert Sherman
Staff Writers: Carol Clingan, Barbara Ensrud,
Susan Feller, Angela D. Goodman, Susan Hillaby,
Joan McCullough, Kathy Ritchell, Kathleen
Shortall, Sandra Streepey
Administrative Assistant: Joyce Pelto
Researchers: Loretta Britten, Muriel Clarke,
Tonna Gibert, Cinda Siler, Reiko Uyeshima

EUROPEAN EDITION

European Editor: George Constable
Assistant European Editor: Kit van Tulleken
Design Consultant: Louis Klein
Chief Designer: Graham Davis
Director of Photography: Pamela Marke
Chief of Research: Vanessa Kramer
Chief Sub-editor: Ilse Gray
Researcher: Jasmine Taylor
Designer: Steve Duwensee
Copy Staff: Katherine Knight

Editorial Production
Production Editor: Ellen Brush
Traffic Co-ordinator: Joanne Holland
Art Department: Julia West

ISBN 7054 0562 1

CO-AUTHOR: **James Underwood Crockett** is an eminent American horticulturist, writer on gardening subjects and, on television, a teacher of plant care and cultivation. A graduate of the University of Massachusetts' Stockbridge School of Agriculture, he has lived in—and cultivated a wide variety of plants in—California, New York, Texas and New England and has served as a consultant to many nurseries and landscapers.

CO-AUTHOR: **Ogden Tanner** is a freelance writer and former editor of THE TIME-LIFE ENCYCLOPAEDIA OF GARDENING. An architectural graduate of Princeton University, he has been associate editor of *House & Home* and assistant managing editor of *Architectural Forum*. He is an amateur botanist and weekend gardener.

CONSULTANT, EUROPEAN EDITION: **Frances Perry** is a well-known gardening authority whose books and broadcasts have gained her an international reputation. She is a member of the Linnean Society, and was the first woman to be elected to the Council of the Royal Horticultural Society; now a Vice-President, she also holds the Society's coveted Victoria Medal of Honour. She has lectured in Australia, New Zealand and America and has collected plants in such diverse areas as Lapland, Africa and South America.

GENERAL EUROPEAN CONSULTANTS: **Roy Hay** is a horticulturist well known for his articles in English publications, including a weekly column in *The Times* newspaper, and for his monthly contribution to the French magazine *L'Ami des Jardins*. He carries on a family gardening tradition—his father, Thomas Hay was Superintendent of the Central Royal Parks in London (1922-1940). Mr. Hay is an Officer of L'Ordre du Merite Agricole of Belgium and France. **André Leroy** is the emeritus chief engineer for the Paris parks and gardens. Since 1958 he has been technical consultant for the magazine *Mon Jardin et Ma Maison*. **Dieneke van Raalte** studied horticulture and landscape gardening at the college of gardening in Fredriksoord in The Netherlands. She is a regular contributor to European gardening magazines and is the author of many Dutch gardening books. **Hans-Dieter Ihlenfeldt** is Professor of Botany at the Institute of General Botany and Botanical Gardening in Hamburg. He is the co-editor of several botanical handbooks and has published in scientific journals. **Heinrich Nothdurft** is chief custodian of the Botanic Garden and lectures at the Institute of Botany in Hamburg. He is co-author of the handbook *Mitteleuropäische Pflanzenwelt* (Flora of Central Europe).

ILLUSTRATOR: **Richard Crist** who provided 111 of the 124 watercolour illustrations for this book, studied at Carnegie Institute of Technology and The Art Institute of Chicago. An amateur botanist, Mr. Crist is author of several children's books. He also provided many of the watercolours for *Vegetables and Fruits* in THE TIME-LIFE ENCYCLOPAEDIA OF GARDENING series.

GENERAL CONSULTANTS: Louise and Cyrus Hyde, Well-Sweep Herb Farm, Port Murray, New Jersey; George A. Kalmbacher, Plant Taxonomist, Brooklyn Botanic Garden, Brooklyn, New York; Joy Logee Martin, Logee's Greenhouses, Danielson, Connecticut; Adelma Grenier Simmons, Caprilands Herb Farm, North Coventry, Connecticut.

THE COVER: Interlacing bands of germander, winter savory and green cotton lavender shape the traditional knot garden at the Brooklyn Botanic Garden. The garden is patterned on one at Hampton Court that probably dates from the reign of Elizabeth I. Between the bands are marble chips, coal and clay shards. The polka dots are dwarf box.

CONTENTS

1 Plants of many virtues
7

2 Beds of flavour and fragrance
25

Picture essay: DISPLAYS OF BEAUTY FROM UTILITARIAN PLANTS
40

3 A garden on the window sill
55

4 Making the most of the harvest
67

5 An illustrated encyclopaedia of herbs
89

APPENDIX

Characteristics of 127 herbs
150

Picture credits and Acknowledgements
152

Bibliography
153

Index
154

Plants of many virtues

Like most people, you probably have a few containers marked *Basil, Marjoram* or *Rosemary* on a kitchen shelf, handy to add sparkle to a sauce or a roast. You may even keep a pot of chives growing fresh on a sunny window sill to snip into cottage cheese or Sunday morning scrambled eggs, or a patch of mint in the garden for fresh mint sauce or iced tea. That, until recently, was the extent of general interest in herbs. But no longer. Today, the experience of one young gardener is more typical.

She saw a classified advertisement under "Herbs" in a gardening magazine and decided to send for a few new plants. Over the next year or two she added to her plot and before long she was growing 30 different culinary herbs near her kitchen door. Furthermore, she learned how to use each of them—at their freshest and most flavourful—to lend a personal touch to her salads, soups and stews; and in the process she also created a few recipes of her own.

Soon she found that herbs provided more than culinary pleasures. In a sunny spot in her garden, she planted her own miniature version of an Elizabethan knot garden, an ingenious bit of horticultural geometry in which the rich greens and silvery greys of germanders and artemisias intertwined around a sundial framed by fragrant thymes and a low lavender hedge. Indoors, she made scented mixtures of dried lavender and other herbs, and created many attractive arrangements of fresh and dried herbs.

Not everyone, of course, gets quite so engrossed in herbs as this gardener. But in recent years a growing number of amateurs have taken up herb growing as a hobby, including many who previously had little experience with plants of any kind.

Undoubtedly, the modern interest in herbs arises partly from a new consciousness of nature and a wish to return to a more natural way of life. It partly also stems from dissatisfaction

Two bearded scholars and an apprentice harvest herbs in a woodcut illustrating a 13th-century German manuscript on medicinal plants. The tree is probably the artist's imaginative rendering of a palm.

with the blandness of some modern foods and a desire to stretch the budget by converting ordinary ingredients into gourmet meals at home. But many people grow herbs simply because it is fun. Of all plants, none offers such great rewards for so little work. Many are decorative, indoors and out, and they are easy to grow and resistant to pests and diseases. Some are highly fragrant, bursting with sweet oils.

Herbs keep on providing their pleasures right through the year. Many kinds can spend the winter indoors growing on a sunny window sill, while the leaves or seeds of others can be dried or frozen for a year-round supply that retains much of its original, garden-fresh taste. Beyond the kitchen, a scented geranium or a potpourri of rose petals brings to a living room reminders of summer that no aerosol room-freshener can match; a sachet of dried lavender or rosemary leaves lends a clean fragrance to a linen drawer and keeps moths away from woollens; wreaths and other dried arrangements lend a festive air to a dinner table, as does a punch bowl flavoured with borage, sweet woodruff or lemon balm.

That so many different and delightful purposes can be served by herbs is not surprising. More than a thousand herbs are still being cultivated in different parts of the world. In the encyclopaedia section of this book (*page 89*) herbs suitable for growing throughout Europe are illustrated and described.

To the ancients, any plant that was not a shrub or a tree was considered a herb—and a suitable candidate for experimentation to see what use might be made of it. To botanists, any plant that dies down to the ground after its growing season and, if it is a perennial, sprouts again the following spring, is technically a herb. But to most people, a herb is a plant, generally small and easy to cultivate, that offers a special usefulness. It may be grown primarily for its fragrance or for its value in cooking or for its historical associations, particularly with medicine—many herbs are practical remedies and many more were once thought to be so.

The broad range of plants that, by one definition or another, could be counted as herbs poses a puzzle for the novice herb gardener. Where do you start? One lady, inspired by a lecture on herbs to plant her own herb garden, sought advice from the gardener-handyman who kept her rose beds in order and her box hedges trimmed. The man put down his fork, rubbed his chin thoughtfully, then said: "Plant a little mint, missus. Then step out of the way so you don't get hurt."

The advice was not as impertinent as it might sound. Of all herbs, common mint is not only among the most popular—

a favourite flavouring for sauces and drinks—but among the most prolific, easy to grow even for people without green fingers. Indeed, unless it is contained within a barricade, it will spread by underground runners and may take over half the garden, cheerfully coming up year after year whether you want it to or not.

To the handyman's terse nominee for instant success might be added a few other reliables among the perennial culinary herbs: for example, chives, tarragon, sage, sweet marjoram and thyme. All can be started from seed (except true French tarragon, which, unlike the inferior-tasting Russian tarragon, rarely produces viable seeds and is usually grown from stem cuttings taken from existing plants). To an impatient gardener-gourmet, however, these perennial herbs and many others, including mint, seem to take forever to grow large enough to harvest when raised from seed. It is easier as well as quicker to buy nursery-grown perennial plants that can be enjoyed in the first year.

To round out a basic herb garden, you will want to include some of the annual and biennial herbs as well, perhaps parsley, basil, summer savory, dill and sweet marjoram. (The latter is a perennial that will not survive the winter in cold climates and therefore is grown as an annual in northern Europe.) These herbs, too, can usually be bought as young plants, but it is not difficult, and considerably cheaper, to start them from seed. Unlike many perennials, the annuals will grow fast enough in one season to provide all the flavouring ingredients you will need.

But a herb garden ought not to be restricted to old favourites used to enhance other foods. Many gardeners include lesser known but equally rewarding edible herbs that in certain dishes may become principal ingredients, not just flavouring.

For those who enjoy salads, there is nothing quite so satisfying as a garden of the herbs that turn everyday salads into extraordinary treats. Among the fresh young leaves that can be used for greens are burnet, borage, lovage, chervil, mustard, orach, sorrel and sweet cicely. Even plants such as chicory and dandelion, often thought of as weeds, are tasty greens; dandelions have been a favourite since medieval times, and the leaves look and taste better if you buy quality seeds and sow them in their own garden bed with enriched soil. Garden cress or nasturtiums—both the leaves and flowers of the latter—add a peppery tang and an attractive garnish; violet leaves and flowers can lend a pleasant perfumed taste; rue satisfies those who like a bitter bite, but be warned that a little goes a long way. The various onions such as garlic, chives, shallots, salad onions, leeks and Egyptian onions add distinctive piquancies of their own.

Many a herb enthusiast devotes part of the herb garden, or a small separate garden, to herbs especially noted for their scents. Walking among such plants on a summer evening can be a heady experience, particularly when you brush against the leaves and release the full aroma of their oils. Some of these oils are useful in flavouring, but the fragrance of almost any of them can be captured for later enjoyment by carefully drying the leaves and flower petals and using them for potpourris, scented pillows and sachets.

Among the mainstays of a scented garden are old-fashioned, sweet-smelling shrub roses, useful as specimen plants or for

PLANNING AND PLANTING AN ELIZABETHAN KNOT GARDEN

The knot garden design on the right is an adaptation of a traditional 16th-century plan. Only three varieties of herbs are needed to create what appears to be a complex pattern of interwoven ribbons, characteristic of this kind of garden. An easy way to lay out this geometric design is illustrated opposite.

When you choose herbs for a knot garden, select compact, low-growing perennials that will tolerate frequent pruning. Among such plants are dwarf lavender, germander, the low-growing artemisia, lemon thyme, hyssop, dwarf sage and santolina. Place the selected plants very close together, at 7.5 to 10 cm (3 to 4 in.) intervals, so that the immediate effect will be one of a continuous ribbon. Then prune them all to a uniform height except where the rows intersect. There the ribbon that is meant to look as if it is on top should be shaped with the pruning shears to give the illusion that it sweeps up and over the lower ribbon.

An established knot garden needs to be manicured on a regular schedule through the growing season in order to keep the ribbon design sharp and clear.

Contrasting colours and textures of the foliage emphasize the over-and-underlapping motif of this design. Before planting a knot garden, make a diagram, colouring in each ribbon.

hedges; lavender and box, for low hedges, borders or beds; some of the pungent mints, and the delicate apple mint; and the more fragrant sages and thymes. There are also lemon verbena and rosemary, which smell as good as they taste, and many kinds of scented geraniums with fragrances suggesting those of roses, lemons and spices. However, bay, lemon verbena, rosemary and scented geraniums will live through the winter only in temperate climates; in cold and exposed northern areas they must be moved indoors in the autumn.

Still other herbs are prized not so much for their flavour or fragrance as for their decorative appearance. At one time or another many had household or medicinal uses, but today

BEAUTY WITH PRACTICALITY

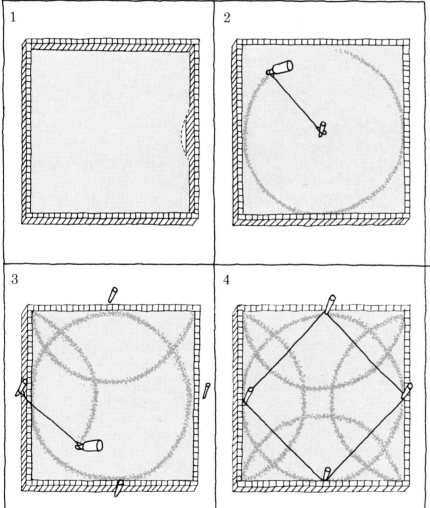

1. *Choose a level, sunny site for the knot garden, ideally one that can be viewed from above. Mark a 3 by 3 metre (10 by 10 ft) square with stakes and string, then edge the bed with bricks set on end and sunk half-way into the soil. Prepare for planting.*

2. *Stretch diagonal strings between the corners and drive a stake where they intersect. Tie a string to the stake and stretch it to the midpoint of one side. Just inside the edging, tie it to a sand-filled bottle. Invert it so sand dribbles out slowly and swing it round, string taut, to mark the circle.*

3. *At the midpoint of each side, drive a stake 30 cm (1 ft) outside the edging. Tie a string to one stake, stretch it to a corner, tie a sand-filled bottle there, and swing it in an arc between two corners; repeat on other sides.*

4. *Move the midpoint stakes just inside the edging and connect them with string. Deposit sand along the string to mark the inner diamond. Plant one kind of herb along the circle line, another on the arcs, a third to outline the diamond. Fill areas between with stones, mulch or low ground-cover plants.*

they are grown mainly for their colours and textures. Notable among these plants are those associated with the so-called grey or silver garden, a speciality since Elizabethan times. Because the leaves have arresting silvery colours—some finely fern-like or softly hairy and appearing nearly white in bright sunlight—they provide stunning focal points in themselves and serve as foils for herbs with darker foliage or bright blooms. The effect of silver plantings can be especially lovely, almost eerie, at night, when the leaves reflect the faintest sky glow; for this reason they are sometimes called moonlight gardens. Among the herbs most often used for this type of garden planting are wormwood, lavender, cotton lavender, dittany, lamb's ears and apple mint.

For contrast with the silver plants, dark green herbs such as low-growing germander are sometimes used in borders. These darker herbs can also make up one strand of a knot design, interwoven with a light-coloured row of dwarf cotton lavender or other light grey plants that can easily be kept neatly clipped. Striking contrasts can also be provided by yellow or orange calendulas, old favourites in herb gardens, or the purple-tinted foliage of basil or red orach. Some purist connoisseurs, however, prefer to keep the whole garden, or one area of their garden, a subtle palette of grey and silver accented only by a few interspersing or background shades of green.

Other specialized gardens are possible with herbs. One type is the bee garden, filled with such plants as bee balm, lemon balm, thyme and borage, which are particularly attractive to honey bees (more than one herb gardener has taken up bee-keeping as a hobby for the tasty honey thus produced). Some herbalists raise plants like woad, bedstraw, tansy, alkanet and rue to make natural vegetable dyes. Others set aside a corner for the ingredients of herbal teas or tisanes—chamomile, catmint, sage, lemon verbena and several of the mints. Still others, delving into history, have modelled herb beds after those of medieval monasteries; a few specialists even try to grow all the herbs mentioned in the Bible or in Shakespeare's plays—and quote appropriate passages as proof.

REFLECTIONS OF DAYS PAST It is such historical associations, perhaps, that give herbs their ultimate appeal. Most of them are old-fashioned plants, not showy crossbreeds of the modern era, and they go back a lot farther than Victorian lavender sachets or Edwardian rose water. Herbs are, in fact, the oldest cultivated garden plants in the world. As such, they offer the interested amateur entertaining glimpses of the way people lived in days gone by, not just hundreds but thousands of years ago. Herbs are living windows on the past.

In the old days, all manner of plants were used not only for their flavours and scents but for almost everything else under the sun—witches' potions, aphrodisiacs, invigorating teas or tisanes, remedies for upset stomachs and falling hair, healing salves for wounds, agents to fend off plague and pestilence, deodorizers to disguise indoor smells. Rudyard Kipling once observed: "Anything green that grew out of the mould/Was an excellent herb to our fathers of old." (And he added wryly: "Half of their remedies cured you dead.")

Until the advent of modern synthetic drugs, scarcely more than a century ago, most medical therapy was based on plants. Ancient records indicate that 5,000 years ago the Sumerians had medicinal uses for caraway and thyme, and a Chinese manuscript of 2700 B.C. listed 365 plants and their health-giving qualities (including a shrub called mahuang, or ephedra, from which chemists derive a modern nasal decongestant). A thousand years before Christ, Egyptian kings fed their slaves and labourers quantities of garlic in the belief that it would make them strong enough to build the pyramids. The Bible suggests that anise and cumin, among others, were herbs of such medicinal value that their seeds were sometimes used in the payment of debts.

In later centuries, the Greeks and Romans expanded and codified the uses of herbs. One of their favourites was an evergreen they called laurel, which grows to tree size on the sunny Mediterranean shores—the same *Laurus nobilis* which is used today under the name of sweet bay or bay laurel to flavour stuffings, milk puddings or a *bouquet garni*. Legend had it that the gods turned the nymph Daphne into a laurel tree to save her from the clutches of Apollo; laurel was regarded as divine, and leafy twigs of it were woven into garlands to crown victorious warriors and athletes as well as eloquent statesmen and poets. At festivals, Greek youths and maidens wore ceremonial garlands of other herbs, including such herbs as parsley, dill and fennel—the latter celebrating the triumphant Battle of Marathon. (Marathon means fennel in Greek; on a field of fennel, the Greeks defeated a Persian army in 490 B.C.)

The Romans, who perpetuated and elaborated many Greek traditions, also used fennel for ceremonial garlands, and valued its fresh, liquorice flavour when it was cooked or chopped into salads. The Romans scattered powdered herbs about their

FROM GARLAND TO STEW

The grey-green foliage of some 70 different herbs shimmers whitely in the sun and appears silvery by moonlight in this grey garden, which was designed as a soothing contrast to the intense colours of nearby flower beds. The planting includes velvety lamb's ears and feathery santolina round a statue of Pan, blue lavender and a group of sages in the front corner and, along the back at the right, a semi-circle of artemisias backed by blue-green junipers.

houses and often burned them as incense—the word perfume comes from the Latin *per fumum*, literally "by smoke". They crushed the flowers of one fragrant herb into their bath water so frequently that it became known as lavender, after the Latin *lavare*, to bathe.

The Greeks and Romans also started the custom, continued throughout Europe and elsewhere until modern times, of using aromatic plants, such as lavender, mint and thyme, as strewing herbs, meant to be spread on floors so their fragrance would conceal household smells. One of the most treasured of the aromatics—in fact, the greatest status symbol among herbs—was saffron, a golden, sweet-scented powder from the flower stigmas of the saffron crocus. Since it takes some 65,000 hand-picked blossoms to make 0.5 kilo (1 lb) of saffron, its use became the epitome of conspicuous consumption, and the wealthy employed it to flavour their food, perfume their banquet halls and dye their robes. The Emperor Nero, with typical extravagance, ordered saffron water to be sprinkled along the road before him when he made his triumphal entries into Rome.

PLANTS THAT SOOTHE

But herbs were prized most of all for their medicinal virtues, real or imagined. The first physicians were avid herbalists; Hippocrates, known as the father of medicine, described some 400 medicinal herbs used in his day, including basil, horehound, rue and sage. The oldest major treatise on the uses of healing plants, called *De Materia Medica*, was compiled in the first century A.D. by Dioscorides, a Greek physician serving with Roman armies. It remained an authoritative work for the next 1,500 years. In Dioscorides' view, herbs were remarkably versatile in their medical applications. For example, mountain rue, which makes some people violently ill, could, in his opinion, cure poisoning, snake-bite, chest pain, hard breathing, coughing, lung inflammation, worms, kidney stones, poor vision, headache, nose-bleed, and pain in the hips, joints and ears. Cress was prescribed to break up carbuncles, cure falling hair, stimulate passion and drive away serpents. Garlic, Dioscorides reported, worked wonders in treating boils, coughs, lice, ulcers, toothache and dog-bites. The lily removed wrinkles, ivy turned the hair black, and cinquefoil soothed or cured toothache, dysentery, liver and lung diseases, poisons, wounds, fear and enchantment.

THE DEW OF THE SEA

Of all the herbs valued by the ancients, rosemary was perhaps the most versatile and beloved. This aromatic shrub with soft, flat, grey-green needles grew on the spray-swept headlands of the Mediterranean—and was christened *ros marinus*, "dew of the sea". It was used in fragrant hedges and borders in the walled gardens of Egypt, Algeria and Spain; the Greeks wore it in festive garlands, burned it at sacrifices and strewed it on floors. Like many other herbs still in use today, it travelled north across Europe and Britain with the Roman legions, becoming a salve for wounds, a love potion, an ingredient in perfumes and embalming fluids, a savoury for meats, and one of 130-odd herbs thought to flavour the Carthusian monks' secret formula for chartreuse liqueur. In the 13th century, Queen Elizabeth of Hungary made famous a concoction called Hungary Water—rosemary, lavender and myrtle steeped in brandy; later rosemary became a constituent of eau-de-Cologne, the German toilet water originally distilled at Cologne.

Throughout history, rosemary appears and reappears as the major herb of sentiment, an evergreen symbol believed to strengthen the bonds of love. Shakespeare's Ophelia declared to Laertes: "There's rosemary, that's for remembrance; pray, love, remember," and the body of the fair Juliet was borne to church covered with sprigs of the herb. In many parts of the world today rosemary still decorates the hearth at Christmas, is slipped into bridal bouquets, and at funerals is placed lovingly in the hands of the dead or planted on their graves.

During the Dark Ages in Europe, the lore of rosemary and many other herbs was kept alive in monasteries, where monks diligently copied recipes from ancient herbals and tended gardens of medicinal plants, which they used in their hospices to treat the sick. Outside monastery walls itinerant herbalists wandered throughout the villages selling herbs, along with secret formulas and incantations to make them work. Around A.D. 800, Charlemagne—King of the Franks and Holy Roman Emperor—compiled an official list of herbs which were to be planted by his subjects for their well-being, and he ordered the same plants to be grown in the royal gardens as well. To him is attributed a classic definition of a herb: "The friend of the physician and the pride of cooks."

With the invention of printing in the 15th century, herbs and herbalists entered their golden age. Over the next two centuries hundreds of different herbals were published, books propounding ancient wisdom spiced with the latest discoveries, theories and opinions. The best-known early work in English was *The Grete Herball* of 1526, a translation of a French book that promised a "parfyt knowledge and understanding of all manner of herbes and there gracyous vertues." Even more celebrated were William Turner's *Herball*, published in three

A Renaissance garden

In 1545 Francesco Bonafede, professor of botany in the medical school of northern Italy's University of Padua, persuaded the local government to establish a Garden of Simples, or herb garden, so his students could practise on the plants of which he preached. Spread over 1.2 hectares (3 acres) leased from a nearby monastery, the garden's modest collection of plants gradually grew over the years.

The garden introduced to Europe such exotica as the potato, the sunflower and the sesame. One of its possessions, a European fan palm, particularly fascinated the poet Goethe, who visited the garden in 1786; he wrote a dissertation on the palm, noting that its leaves were different in form, bottom and top. Goethe's palm still stands, labelled as such. And on marble tablets at the garden's entrance can be seen Professor Bonafede's rules for the garden's use: visitors are cautioned not to break stems or branches, pick flowers or collect seeds—on pain of being fined, imprisoned or banished.

A 16th-century plan of the Spaldo Terzo, or Third Bed, below, identifies the garden's plantings in terms that no longer correspond to modern plant names (and are, moreover, almost illegible).

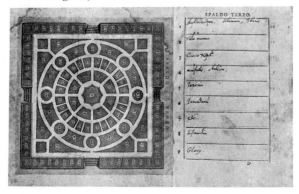

In an 1854 view of the garden, the main gate is at the top, flanked by a semi-circular row of greenhouses that no longer exist. During this period, the garden contained 16,000 kinds of plants, more than it holds today.

In the modern garden, a circular greenhouse protects Goethe's palm, now grown to great size. The semi-circular beds directly in front of it hold the garden's only remaining herbs, originally its raison d'être.

Terraced plots of herbs now growing in the garden include spear-like mullein, lower right, and, beside it, blue-flowered hyssop. To the left of the hyssop is white-flowered henbane and, upper left, horseradish.

19

instalments between 1551 and 1562, and *The Herball or Generall Historie of Plantes* completed in 1597 by John Gerard, an English barber-surgeon with a passion for gardening and an eye for fame. (Hired to translate a Belgian work, he rearranged it and, with the help of 1,800 woodcuts borrowed from a German botanical treatise, published it as his own.) In 1640, John Parkinson, another gardener-physician, who was official herbalist to Charles I, published his *Theatrum Botanicum*, a stupendous work that examined the characteristics and uses of no fewer than 3,800 plants.

AN ELIZABETHAN HERBAL The most popular herbal of all, however, was a slimmer volume by a 33-year-old apothecary and astrologer named Nicholas Culpeper, who in 1649 outraged England's learned College of Physicians by translating their precious pharmacopoeia—an exclusive tome consulted only by doctors who could read Latin —into plain English, with critical comments of his own, for ordinary folk to share. The brash Culpeper followed in 1653 with his bestseller, *The English Physician*, which bore the clarion, non-stop title: *An Astrological Discourse of the Vulgar Herbs of this Nation being a Compleat Method of Physick whereby a man may preserve his Body in health; or cure himself being sick, for three pence charge, with such things one-ly as grow in England, they being most fit for English Bodies.* A spirited blend of traditional medicine, folklore, astrology and magic, it listed 369 plants along with detailed advice on where to find each, how to recognize it, which celestial body it was governed by and the uses it might have.

Culpeper was not only brash; he had a ready wit with which to present an astonishing amount of information—and misinformation. About a concoction that incorporated mustard seed, he wrote: "Let old men and women make much of this Medicine, and they will either give me thanks or manifest ingratitude." And at another point in his herbal he noted: "Sage is of excellent use to help the Memory, warming and quickening the senses; and the Conserve made of the Flowers is used to the same purpose."

Among the more curious gospels preached by Culpeper and others in their herbals was the Doctrine of Signatures, which held that the proper medicinal use of a plant could be divined from its appearance. Thus the signature attributed to a plant known as lungwort—vaguely lung-shaped leaves covered with whitish spots—supposedly indicated that it could be used for treatment of diseased, i.e. spotted, lungs. It was steeped in infusions and quaffed by uncounted numbers of people for the treatment of chest colds and whooping cough. In the same way wild pansies (heartsease) were regarded as a potent base for a heart tonic because they have heart-shaped leaves; hollow-stalked plants like garlic were believed salutary for ailments of the windpipe; the flowers of eyebright, thought to resemble bloodshot eyes, were used to make eye lotions for preventing blindness and curing cataracts.

Even odder, though more innocent, meanings were attached to herbs in the Language of Flowers, an elaborate code of symbols that started in the Middle Ages and reached its peak in romantic Victorian days. In this courtly and circumspect method of communication, a lady and her suitor—presumably both armed with the same list of plants and their assigned meanings, not to mention an ability to recognize different plants on sight—could conduct discreet conversations by exchanging appropriate flowers or sprigs.

An eager swain, for example, might open the dialogue by sending his love a sprig of myrtle (symbol, Fragrance; code words, "Be my love"). Or he might pick vervain (Enchantment: "You have bewitched me") or fraxinella (Ardour: "My heart is afire"). If the lady was unimpressed, she might send back lavender (Sad Refusal: "I like you, but only as a friend"); mint (Homeliness: "Find a spouse of your own age and background"); aconite (Dislike: "Your attentions are unwelcome"); or—the unkindest cut of all—the lowly dandelion (Absurdity: "I find your presumption laughable"). If the suitor was undismayed by such chilly responses, he might attempt to rescue the romance with burdock (Persistence: "I shall not be discouraged"). The lady, in turn, could reply with borage (Brusqueness: "Your attentions only embarrass me"); chamomile (Fortitude: "I admire your courage; do not despair"); golden rod (Indecision: "Allow me time to decide"); or marjoram (Maidenly Innocence: "Your passion sends blushes to my cheeks"). If all went well, a suitor both ardent and tenacious might one day be so fortunate as to experience the spine-tingling moment when the postman arrived with a little envelope containing angelica (Inspiration: "Your love is my guiding star").

Such fripperies as the Language of Flowers were far from the concerns of the first English colonists who went to the shores of America. With them went seeds, roots and cuttings of their favourite household herbs, to be planted in their gardens. Sometimes these were combined with native herbal medicines adopted from the Indians' stock. Every Puritan housewife knew, in John Parkinson's phrase, "what Herbes and Fruits were fit, eyther for meate or medicine, for Use or Delight". She could

It was common practice in England as late as the 19th century to strew aromatic herbs such as marjoram, mint or sweet flag on the floors of modest dwellings and great public buildings alike, in the belief that the scent prevented the spread of disease. During plagues, the sale of such strewing herbs quickened. But the importance attached to them is perhaps best indicated by the prominence given, for centuries, to the role of the appointed herb strewer in the coronations of English kings and queens. Ladies of the court competed fiercely for the honour of leading the royal procession to Westminster Abbey, scattering herbs from a satin-lined gilt basket—a ritual that was intended to purify the air surrounding the monarch. Though the custom died out at the end of the 19th century, Queen Elizabeth II observed the ritual by accepting a nosegay of aromatic herbs at her 1953 coronation.

grow almost every plant she needed: flavourings, garnishes and "sallets" for the table; nosegays and strewing herbs for freshening chambers; repellents for ants, moths, mice and snakes; dyes to colour woollens and teasel for teasing up their naps; soothing hot teas of chamomile, sage or wintergreen; plasters, salves and lotions for treating cuts, relieving coughs or toothaches, or easing the pains of childbirth; and, inevitably, herbs for laying out the dead.

Among the colonial New England housewife's "simples"— old reliables used by themselves—were balm for bee stings, lungwort and horehound for throat and lung ailments, tansy for treating worms. For more complex "unknown guests", as ailments were called, a package remedy was often deemed appropriate, on the theory that a combination of herbs could purge "both upwards and downwards" by inducing sneezing, sweating, vomiting and laxative action—sometimes all at once. If the patient recovered, the "imbalance" had been eliminated. If he did not, it was believed, God had obviously called him. Some early American recipes were formidable: "Take for a cough or stitch upon a cold, Wormwood, Sage, Marygolds, and Crabs-claws boiled in posset-drink [hot milk curdled by ale or wine and spiced] and drunk off very warm." Or: "For wind Collick, take Summer Savory, Angelica, Sweet Tansy and Elecampane; for back pains, make a syrup of Borage or Comphrey and add Brandy and Gunpowder to taste."

NOSTRUMS FOR ONE AND ALL

Other countries had their own folk medicines. Old Dutch treatments for asthma, for example, included sleeping on the dried flowers of pearl everlasting, chewing calamus root, smoking the leaves of mullein, drinking teas made of horehound, hyssop, sage and yarrow, and sipping a potion made by steeping "four quarts of huckleberries for four days in two gallons of good gin". Dutch immigrants to the United States took their herbal remedies with them, and by the 19th century commercial herb farms, started modestly by religious communities of Shakers, had begun to supply home remedies that city dwellers could no longer conveniently grow. Before long, hundreds of patent medicines, root tonics and snake oils, most of them using herbs in the ingredients, were advertised in American newspapers and sold from door to door.

It is only in this century that herbs have been largely replaced by synthetic drugs in the manufacture of medicines. In fact, herbal remedies remain in the prescription books of the many European apothecaries and herbalists, and most village markets, particularly in southern Europe, display bunches of medicinal herbs for use in remedies that have been treasured for centuries. Their healing qualities may be doubtful, but they seldom have any side effects.

With the evolution of modern medicine, the use of such remedies declined. But herbs still serve mankind in a prodigious number of ways. Many are the sources for modern drugs. Among them are the heart stimulant digitalis from the foxglove, the pain-killing morphine from the poppy, tranquillizers from valerian, and burn ointments from the aloe plant.

The worldwide manufacture of cosmetics, foods and drinks also owes much to herbs. Their fragrant oils are used in making soaps, perfumes and lotions. Massage ointments get their heating-soothing action (and "healing" smell) from substances such as menthol and thymol found in wormwood, mint and thyme. Bitter wormwood also flavours alcoholic drinks such as vermouth and absinthe, although it is poisonous in concentrated form; anise seeds impart their liquorice taste to pastis, caraway goes into kümmel, mint makes crème de menthe and angelica helps to flavour gin. Borage makes a pleasant addition to chilled summer fruit cups.

Above all, herbs still go into food. Today, thousands of tonnes of them, raised on farms throughout the world, lend their flavours to nearly everything we eat: sausages, frank-furters and other processed meats; sauces, salads and stews; buns, biscuits, cheeses and confections; and—in flavours and mixtures to tingle the most jaded palates—every mustard, relish, chutney, pickle, mayonnaise, meat sauce and condiment on the supermarket shelf. Not to mention the herb plot in your garden or the pots of fresh herbs on your window sill or even those bottles of dried herbs in your kitchen—all of which help to make a meal worth lingering over and provide a challenge to the imagination of every enterprising cook.

THE BITTER AND THE SWEET

A BARRICADE AGAINST POXES
In Elizabethan England many herbs were thought efficacious in warding off disease. Ladies and gentlemen who were forced to frequent streets and public halls of London—hardly models of cleanliness in those days—carried nosegays of lavender, wormwood and other scented leaves, which they sniffed periodically to fend off unpleasant odours and, they hoped, the plagues and poxes that might lurk behind them. Eminent judges in robes and powdered wigs, obliged to share their courtrooms with unsavoury criminals on trial, kept similar herbal bouquets handy. And everywhere in those days before preservatives and refrigeration, herbs and spices were liberally sprinkled on food—often in quantities and combinations that would make a modern gourmet gag— to disguise the flavour of tainted if not downright rotten meat.

Beds of flavour and fragrance

Centuries ago, when Columbus and other mariners of Genoa were making the city a renowned seaport, many of its sailors relied on their noses to tell them they were near home, for long before they saw land they could smell the thyme blanketing their native Ligurian hills. Liguria, like the other headlands of the Mediterranean, was the home not only of accomplished seamen, but of thyme, rosemary and many of the other plants classified as herbs. They evolved in this sun-warmed, rocky environment, and that fact tells much about the growing conditions they need: sunshine and well-drained soil.

Not that herbs are fussy. Most grow nearly anywhere that is sunny and not too wet. And even these requirements are not essential for all herbs. Some, mint and parsley among them, tolerate partial shade, and shade is best for woodland herbs like sweet woodruff. But for most of the more popular herbs used today, at least five hours of direct sunlight a day is required, and the availability of sun should determine a herb garden's position. If you have space for a sunny, south-facing bed near the kitchen door you will be twice blessed; you can plant your herb garden there, just a few steps away whenever you need a few flavourful sprigs of tarragon or thyme. Otherwise, site your herbs in or next to a vegetable garden, in pots on a sunny patio, along a garden path or even bordering the front drive. Herbs can be decorative as well as edible if they are arranged with foliage patterns and colours in mind, and they serve admirably as borders, ground covers or accents tucked into odd spaces in a rock garden or between terrace flagstones. Avoid planting them near a mature tree, however; not just because of the shade, but because shallow, far-reaching tree roots make digging difficult and soon infiltrate the herbs, robbing them of nutrients and moisture.

Just as important as sunlight is soil with proper drainage;

A honey bee feasts on the pollen-laden flowers of a chive plant. Ordinarily grown as flavouring for food, it is one of several herbs with blossoms so decorative that they warrant a place in the flower garden.

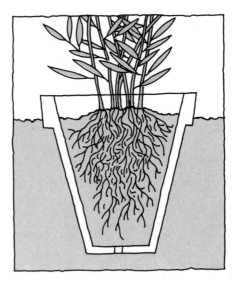

RESTRAINING THE WANDERERS
Herbs—such as tarragon, bee balm and mint—whose roots spread rapidly can be held in check by the walls of a clay flower pot or galvanized bucket with the bottom removed. Sink the pot or bucket into the soil so deep that only 2.5 cm (1 in.) of the rim extends above the ground. Partly fill the pot or bucket with garden soil and insert the plant; then add more soil, firming it around the roots with your fingers until the soil level matches that of the surrounding garden.

only a few herbs, such as sweet flag, sweet woodruff and horse-radish, can survive moist soil around their roots for long. The ideal site is a porous, slightly sandy soil or a gentle slope; any low place where rain water collects and does not drain away quickly should be suspect. If you are not sure that the drainage is adequate at a potential garden site, dig a hole 45 centimetres (1½ ft) wide and equally deep, and fill it with water. If any water is still visible in the hole an hour later, look for another site. If there is no better place that has sufficient sun, do not despair. You can improve the drainage by either digging down or building up, as described on pages 29 and 30.

LAYING OUT THE BED
A simple rectangular plot is the easiest to plant and maintain. It is also the easiest to make into a raised bed, a useful device in any garden and an especially valuable one with herbs. A rectangular plot can be readily divided into rows or beds to suit herbs with various growing habits and requirements. But plan the layout before you plant. It is important to separate perennial herbs from annuals, so that you will not trample on the perennials when you prepare the soil and plant your annuals each year. A plan will also make it easier to allocate shade to shade-tolerant herbs, and to isolate such rampant growers as mint and bee balm, which are apt to encroach on other herbs. Within individual beds you can measure, before planting, the space each kind of herb will require when fully grown. You can also arrange plants according to their respective heights at maturity, placing the taller ones such as dill, fennel and lovage towards the north side of the herb bed so that they do

not shade the shorter herbs such as parsley, chives or thyme.

If all this planning strikes you as forbidding, consider the kind of helpful guidance that was given to herb gardeners of old. In ancient Rome, Pliny based much of his horticultural advice on his belief in the existence of strong friendships and enmities among plants. Rue dislikes basil, he proclaimed, and hyssop simply cannot get along with the radish. But savory is a good friend of the onion, and the most sociable gathering of all is a bed full of those extroverts, coriander, dill, mallow and chervil.

In medieval times, the superstitions took a darker turn. Those who had trouble growing parsley were told they were too good for it, since parsley would thrive only for the wicked. To overcome his natural goodness, the herb gardener was directed to sow parsley seeds on Good Friday by the light of a rising moon—and furthermore, to sow four times as much as he would need, since parsley had to make nine trips to the devil before it could come up out of the ground. (As is noted elsewhere in this book parsley *is* extremely slow to germinate.)

Consider working convenience when establishing the dimensions of your herb garden. A single rectangular bed bordering a sunny side of the house can be as wide as 1 metre (3 ft) and still keep all plants within reach. If you have access to two sides, a bed 1.5 metres (5 ft) wide can be comfortably tended. A single bed 1.5 metres (5 ft) square provides a modest start, but place it so that you will have the option of adding a similar second bed either in front or to one side, separated by a path 60 centimetres (2 ft) wide. In time you may want four beds forming a square with intervening paths. For a more formal, geometrical appearance, this basic pattern can be varied in a number of ways. One of the simplest is to move the corner beds out by 30 centimetres (1 ft) or so and notch their inner corners to allow room for a small centrepiece bed as a focal point. Another attractive alternative is called a goosefoot design, in which the paths radiate like the rays of the sun from one corner of a square bed.

When you have chosen a site and a design for your herb garden, mark its outlines with lengths of string tied to stakes. Now you are ready to start preparing the beds—in a way that will help your herbs to grow best.

One of the most misleading statements made about herbs is that they thrive in poor soil. To be sure, some, such as thyme and rosemary, cling tenaciously to meagre, rocky crevices along their native Mediterranean coastline, while others seem to

PATTERNS THAT SAVE WORK

become less fragrant if, to encourage foliage growth, they are fed a nitrogen-rich fertilizer. But, while herbs are less demanding than the hybrids of the rose or vegetable garden, they will not do well in really poor soil. Under such impoverished conditions they will grow a few spindly centimetres and then go on strike.

As a general rule, herbs thrive in loose soil that is enriched with a moderate amount of organic matter or fertilizer to supply nutrients and that is close to neutral (pH 7) on the acid-alkaline pH scale. Almost any soil will benefit from the addition of up to one third organic matter, such as moss peat or compost, well mixed to the depth of a fork, or deeper; it will add body to a light, sandy soil so that it will hold more moisture and nutrients near the roots of the plants, and it will also loosen up a heavy clay soil so that water and air can penetrate more easily. Moss peat has little nutritive value and, unless the soil is already fertile, it should be supplemented with a fertilizer such as well-rotted farmyard manure, which will also help to lighten the soil. Manure is available in dry, pre-packaged form at most local garden centres.

If you use compost, nutrients as well as body will be supplied. You can make rich compost from garden waste. You

THREE CONCRETE-BLOCK MINI-GARDENS

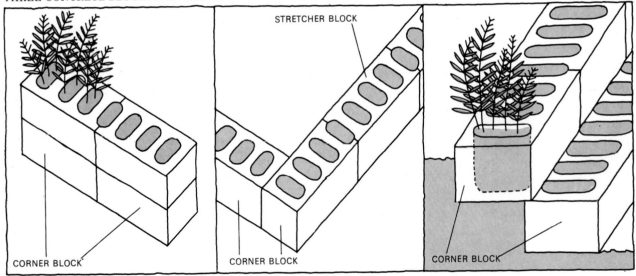

For a simple herb trough, stack perforated building blocks one on top of another. Fill the cores of the lower tier with pebbles for drainage, cover with aluminium or plastic screening and fill the upper cores with soil. Then plant herbs.

To form a herb border, use a combination of corner blocks and stretcher blocks (blocks with half cores at both ends). Set the blocks directly on the ground, or dig a trench and bury them half way. Fill with soil and plant.

To make tiers for a gentle incline, stack blocks, starting at the bottom. Working on one level at a time, dig a shallow trench and sink the blocks into it. Make no more than three tiers, and overlap the blocks about 2.5 cm (1 in.).

will need a frame or container to hold the mixture while it ferments; drive three or four 1.2 metre (4 ft) stakes 30 centimetres (1 ft) into the ground and wrap small-mesh wire fencing around them to form an enclosure 1 metre (3 ft) high. Inside it, blend dead leaves, grass clippings, weeds, and other vegetable matter such as beet or carrot tops. On top of each 10 to 15 centimetre (4 to 6 in.) layer of this organic material, sprinkle three or four handfuls of a high-nitrogen garden fertilizer such as 10:10:10, a mixture of compounds providing 10 per cent nitrogen, 10 per cent phosphorus and 10 per cent potassium. The strong nitrogen content is beneficial because it feeds the bacteria that break down the raw organic material into rich, brown compost; the high proportion of phosphorus is important in building strong roots and stems, and the potassium helps the perennial herbs to resist winter cold. Add a dusting of ground limestone to reduce acidity, and blanket each layer with 5 centimetres (2 in.) of soil to speed the heat-decay process inside. Alternatively, sprinkle each layer with a proprietary compost accelerator, according to the manufacturer's instructions. Make the top slightly concave so that it will catch rain; keep the pile moist and turn it over every month or six weeks. In six months or less you will have a dark, crumbly, well-rotted mixture ideal as an organic additive for preparing your herb beds, and for refreshing them in subsequent growing seasons.

MODIFYING SOIL CHEMISTRY

To make sure your soil has the right chemistry for the herbs you are planting, test it before preparing the beds. You can determine the acidity or alkalinity—pH—of your soil with a kit sold at many garden centres, or by sending a soil sample to your local agricultural advice bureau for analysis. Most herbs will do well in a range of 6.0 to 7.5, measured on a scale that runs from 0 at the acid end through 7 for neutral to 14 at the alkaline end. If your soil is too acid for the herbs you plan to grow, work 2.5 kilos (5 lb) of finely ground limestone into each 10 square metres (approximately 100 sq. ft) of planting area to raise the pH half to one point. If the soil is too alkaline, use 250 grams (8 oz) of ground sulphur, or 1.5 kilos (3 lb) of iron sulphate or aluminium sulphate, to lower the pH an equal amount; the ground sulphur is slower acting but it has a longer-lasting effect on the soil.

If you have soil with exceptionally poor drainage, say with an impermeable layer of hard pan beneath the surface, you may be able to improve it by installing a percolation layer. Dig down 30 centimetres (1 ft) or more, setting aside clumps of turf, dark topsoil and lighter subsoil in separate heaps. In the bottom of the excavated bed, spread a 7.5 centimetre (3 in.) layer of heavy gravel or brick rubble. Make a layer of the turf clumps on top of it, then add some of the subsoil, generously mixed with sand. Finally, cover the bed with the topsoil. mixed with compost or moss peat and any other necessary additives required by the herbs.

An easier way to assure good drainage, for the herb beds is to raise them at least partly above ground level. A raised bed is an old tradition in herb gardening—in fact, it was called a "bed" because it looked like one designed for sleeping in. Almost regardless of the kind of soil below it, a raised bed guarantees the drainage these plants need. Excess water will trickle down at least to ground level and drain away. The

A BEGINNER'S GARDEN

1. *The 1 by 2 metre (3 by 6 ft) herb garden illustrated on the right is raised for easy access. Vary the dimensions as required, but keep width to 1 metre (3 ft) or less. Construct the frame from 2.5 by 20 cm (1 by 8 in.) timber with galvanized nails or angle brackets. Paint it with wood preservative, not creosote.*

2. *Remove turf from an area the size of the frame in a site that receives at least five hours of sun daily. Dig over the soil. Work in 5 cm (2 in.) of compost or 7.5 cm (3 in.) of moss peat, 225 grams (8 oz) of 5:10:5 fertilizer for every square metre (10 sq. ft), and limestone or sulphur to correct the pH factor (page 29). Dig a 7.5 cm (3 in.) deep trench around the plot, lower the frame into it and add enough topsoil to fill.*

3. *The following basic herbs are enough for the needs of a family of four: six parsley plants, one large clump (or two small ones) of chives, six each of basil and dill, one each of sage, marjoram, tarragon, thyme and rosemary, and three mints—one each of spearmint, peppermint, and apple mint.*

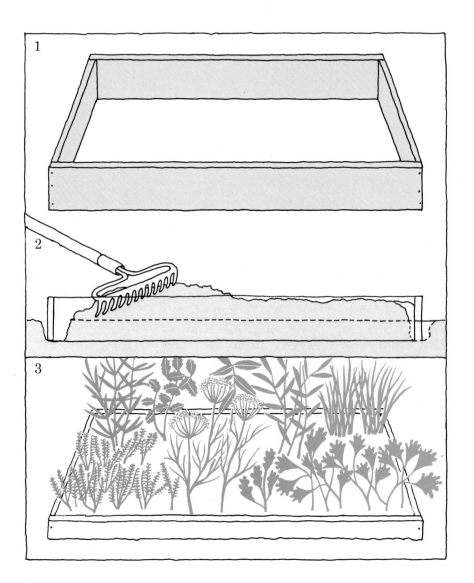

elevated soil will also become dry and warm somewhat earlier in the spring, often allowing planting days ahead of the surrounding ground-level soil.

There are other good reasons for constructing raised planting areas in a herb garden. They keep the garden neat, providing well-defined places for planting and holding everything in its place. Annuals can be planted each year in one raised bed, while perennials can remain undisturbed in another. Plants that naturally have a tidy appearance, such as cotton lavender or germander, can be used along the edges, with more unruly growers like horseradish and wormwood set behind them. Free-ranging plants such as the mints can be grown in their own separate beds, whose sides will block and contain their invasive roots. Similarly, the raised sides stop grass and other ground covers from moving in, and the gravel or stone chips of garden paths are not scuffed in among the plants. Nor do you need to bend over quite so far when you weed or harvest the herbs.

RAISED BEDS

Above-ground beds pay aesthetic dividends, too. The geometrical pattern of the garden, emphasized by the three-dimensional look of the raised edges, is pleasing to the eye, and such a garden looks orderly and attractive at any time of year, whether it is full of growing plants or not. If the beds are raised 30 centimetres (1 ft) or more, you can widen their edges to provide benches where you can sit while you enjoy the fragrance.

Almost any kind of container can be used to make a raised bed for herbs—a long planting trough, a stone retaining wall, even hollow concrete building blocks or flue tiles filled with soil. Higher beds can be edged with boards, 5 centimetres (2 in.) thick and 25 or 30 centimetres (10 or 12 in.) wide, held together with angle brackets. Heavy timbers or railway sleepers, which make durable frames for raised beds, can be laid on the surface of the ground and held in position with stakes.

EDGING THAT LASTS

Rotproof edging can be built with stones, rectangular pieces of slate set on edge, or strips of asbestos building board cut to order with a special saw. One of the simplest permanent edgings, both attractive and traditional, is made with plain bricks either set on end in a shallow trench or laid horizontally two or three courses high. Wooden boards, approximately 20 to 25 centimetres (8 to 10 in.) wide, can also be used but are not as durable; they should be protected against rot with two coats of wood preservative. Avoid creosote, which is toxic to plants. As you dig to prepare the soil in the beds, sink the boards around the edges 5 to 7.5 centimetres (2 to 3 in.) below ground level to keep them in place, leaving the remainder of the width extending above the ground. Finish preparing the soil inside, mixing in any necessary nutrients and organic matter and adding extra soil if necessary, so that the soil surface is about 2.5 centimetres (1 in.) below the top of the boards.

Most of this preparatory work is best done a season in advance. Since additives such as limestone and sulphur do not take full effect for months, it is a good idea to incorporate them into the beds in the autumn for spring planting or in the spring for autumn planting. Preparing beds ahead also allows time for organic additives such as compost or manure to blend into the soil in a form most usable to the plants, and it gives the beds time to settle naturally under rainfall to their permanent level before the planting season arrives.

If you live in northern Europe, where the climate is temperate, you should be ready to plant herbs soon after frost leaves the ground in spring; in mild parts of southern Europe, you can plant at virtually any time of year, although many gardeners favour autumn planting because the relatively cool season ahead permits the plants to become well established before the

TRANSPLANTING SEEDLINGS

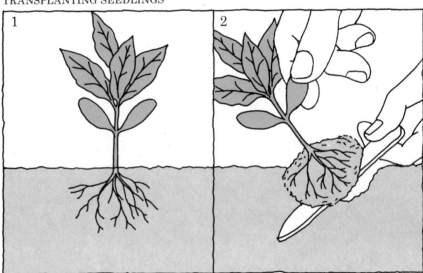

Separate and transplant seedlings grown in pots or seedbeds when they are about 5 cm (2 in.) tall and after they have produced two pairs of true leaves above the rounded pair of seed leaves. Moisten the soil sufficiently to permit easy separation of the seedlings with minimum disturbance to their roots.

Gently grasp one of the rounded seed leaves—never hold a young plant by its delicate stem—and use the pointed end of a plant label to pry up the roots. Still holding the plant by a seed leaf, carefully lift the seedling out of the ground. To minimize transplanting shock, replant the herb immediately.

arrival of hot summer weather. Wait until the soil has dried enough to be crumbly when dug to the depth of a fork, then turn over once more the settled beds you prepared some months earlier. Break up clods of earth with the back of the fork, and rake out any loose stones that turn up. If the soil is still a little too heavy or too light, or if you are renewing beds used the previous year, dig in an additional 2.5 centimetres (1 in.) of compost or 5 to 7.5 centimetres (2 to 3 in.) of moss peat. If the soil lacks nutrients, dig in a quick-acting balanced chemical fertilizer. The best choice for most herbs is 5:10:5. Mix the fertilizer into the soil at a rate of 1.5 to 2 kilos (3 to 4 lb) per 10 square metres (approximately 100 sq. ft). If your soil needs only phosphorus, you can substitute 1.5 to 3 kilos (3 to 6 lb) of bone-meal per 10 square metres (approximately 100 sq. ft). Or, if only potassium is called for, you can supply all that most herbs need with a scattering of wood ashes from a fireplace.

STARTING FROM SCRATCH

Most herbs can be bought in the form of young plants ready to set out in the garden, but you may choose to raise annuals from seed. Sow them directly outdoors as soon as the ground can be prepared. A simple way to space plants properly is to mark off a grid by pressing a hoe handle into the soil at the intervals specified for mature plants; at each intersection of the lines thus made, sprinkle a few seeds and cover them with a little soil.

A rule of thumb is to cover seeds to a depth equal to two or three times their diameter; tiny seeds like those of thyme are simply dropped on the surface of the loose soil to work their way in. Press down the soil around the seeds with the heel of your hand to firm it into little saucer-like depressions, which will gather water. The depressions will also mark the places where you should be careful about weeding until the seedling herbs can be identified. Moisten the bed with a fine spray from a garden hose and keep it moist but not soggy until the seedlings germinate. Hessian, cheesecloth or muslin, laid temporarily over the beds and anchored with stones, will hold moisture in sunny or windy gardens and will keep heavy rain from washing seeds away: just make sure that you remove the covering as soon as the seedlings germinate.

THINNING TO TASTE

When the seedlings are about 5 centimetres (2 in.) high or have developed their first pairs of true leaves (recognizable as those of the species), snip off all but the strongest plant in each cluster of seedlings—and eat those discarded as the first tender taste of your garden herbs.

Many gardeners make two or three sowings of herbs such

as dill and fennel at 10-day to three-week intervals until early summer, to extend the season when fresh crops of leaves or seeds will be available for picking.

The seeds of some herbs—annuals such as dill and borage, and also perennials such as thyme and hyssop—can be sown in late autumn after warm weather is past. They will remain dormant over winter and come up the following spring.

For a head start with the seeds of slow-growing perennials such as winter savory and thyme, plant seeds indoors in pots four to six weeks before the last frost is expected. Moisten the soil by standing the container in a tray of water until the surface becomes slightly damp, then plant the seeds. Cover the container with plastic cling film and set it away from bright light in a place where the temperature will remain between 18° and 24°C (65° and 75°F). When the seeds have germinated, generally in a week to 15 days (the reluctant parsley may take five weeks), remove the plastic and set the containers on a sunny window sill. Turn them every day to maintain an even growth rate and to keep the seedlings from leaning towards the light. Before the seedlings become crowded, transplant them to individual containers or thin them out by clipping off all but the strongest plants in the batch.

MOVING SEEDLINGS

To transplant, lift them out of the containers one by one, using a plant label to pry up the root system of each with a little ball of soil. Steady the top of the plant with a gentle hold on a leaf—never touch the tender stem—and lower the root ball into a prepared hole. You can transplant seedlings into sectioned plastic trays, clay or plastic pots or peat pots. Peat pots are eventually set in the garden with the plants; the roots grow through the sides of the disintegrating peat pots and into the surrounding soil with a minimum amount of transplant shock.

TEMPERING THE SHOCK

When the weather has moderated sufficiently, depending on each plant's tolerance for cold as well as your local climate, firm the seedlings gently into the soil and make a little, saucer-like depression around each to catch and hold moisture, setting the plants no deeper than they were growing indoors. Stick identification markers next to the plants and water them with a fine mist from a garden hose or watering can. To ease the abrupt change from indoor to outdoor conditions, try to transplant on a mild, overcast day, and shade the tender seedlings for a day or two with cheesecloth held above them on stakes, or with a leafy twig pushed into the soil on the south side of the plants. (Nursery-grown plants of sturdier perennials such as tarragon, rosemary or sage, however, do not require such precautions and can be set into the ground at almost any time after purchase.)

Once the plants are growing in the garden, make sure they get enough moisture. Never let the soil become completely dry. A common mistake with herbs is to water them too frequently and too shallowly with a fast, once-over from the hose. The best rule is not to water unless you can see leaves beginning to wilt. Then water deeply and thoroughly, either spraying patiently and slowly until the soil is moist to a depth of 30 centimetres (1 ft) or stringing a perforated plastic hose through the plant bed and letting it run for an hour or two.

To shade the soil and thus help it to retain moisture, and to

PROPAGATING BY DIVISION

1. *Herbs that grow in clumps and multiply rapidly—chives, valerian, tarragon—should be divided every few years into smaller clumps, either in early spring when top growth is young, or in autumn when the plants are dormant. Moisten the soil; loosen, it round the clump with a fork then raise the root ball.*

2. *Shake the soil off the roots or wash it away gently with the hose. Separate the matted roots with your fingers, using a combing action that breaks as few roots as possible.*

3. *Pull the root clump gently apart, discarding the old centre. You may have to cut tougher, woody plants, such as tansy or winter savory, with a sharp knife.*

4. *Dig new planting holes large enough to accommodate the root clumps without crowding. Place a 5 to 10 cm (2 to 4 in.) layer of compost—or a mixture of 5:10:5 fertilizer and moss peat—in each hole. Reset the plants at their previous growing level. Fill the holes with soil, firming it around the roots with your fingers, then tamping the ground with your foot.*

smother most weeds before they start, many herb gardeners apply a summer mulch around the plants when they are about 15 centimetres (6 in.) tall. Sawdust, half-decayed leaves, ground bark or chunky moss peat will do the job without holding so much moisture that the plants rot. Spread the mulch 2.5 to 5 centimetres (1 to 2 in.) thick between the plants, tapering off to 12 millimetres ($\frac{1}{2}$ in.) near the stems.

That is all the care most herbs need, except for pulling an occasional weed. Some of the larger, faster-growing plants—such as dill, fennel, lovage and chervil, for instance—will benefit from a scattering of 5:10:5 fertilizer next to them when they are about 30 centimetres (1 ft) tall. Few herbs are attacked by diseases, and their fragrant oils, which make them so attractive to humans, seem to repel most insects. Insecticides are seldom necessary, and in any case are best not used on edible herbs. If you do find that insects are nibbling on your herbs, knock them off with a stiff spray from the garden hose.

Once started properly, a herb garden should flourish year after year with a little care—and vigilance—on your part. Many annual and biennial herbs—dill, mustard and caraway, for example—will perpetuate themselves if you allow some of your plants to produce and drop their seeds, though you will have to learn to recognize the tiny wayward seedlings so that you can transplant them to their proper places.

Perennials such as chives, tarragon and bergamot can be multiplied by division when they become large. In fact, they will be more vigorous as well as more numerous if they are dug up, divided and replanted about every third year. In warm southern regions, pull or cut such plants apart after they have flowered; farther north it is better to divide root clumps in very early spring while they are still dormant, giving the new plants a long growing season to develop strong root systems.

PROPAGATING BY DIVISION To divide an old plant, dig deeply around it with a fork and lift it out of the ground with as much of the root ball intact as possible; then pull the plant apart with your hands. You may have to cut some of the roots apart with a large knife or a sharp spade. Discard the old and compacted centre section of the clump and place each young outer section in a hole of ample size in a bed that has been dug to a depth of 30 centimetres (1 ft) or more and conditioned with compost, moss peat and a scattering of 5:10:5 fertilizer. Set the plants at the depth at which they were previously growing and fill in the hole with soil, firming it well with your feet and soaking it with water when you have finished.

If you are dividing growing plants in summer or autumn, cut their stems back by half so that their root systems, abbreviated in the process of dividing, will have less top growth to support. If you plan to pot sections of chives or parsley to bring indoors for fresh flavouring in the winter, pot them in late summer but let them stand outdoors for a month or two before moving them to a sunny window sill in the house.

Many perennial herbs—lavender, rosemary, wormwood, lemon balm and others—can be propagated from stem cuttings, a method that leaves the parent plants undisturbed. Stem cuttings can be taken in spring or early summer. Cut off a 10 to 15 centimetre (4 to 6 in.) tip of a leaf stem, choosing one that is firm but not hardened and woody, and making the cut

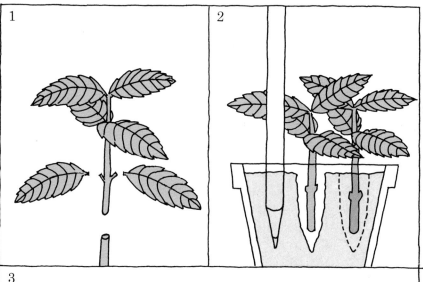

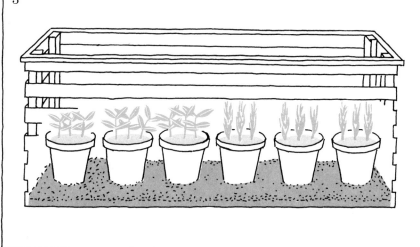

TAKING STEM CUTTINGS

1. *Cut 10 to 15 cm (4 to 6 in.) long young, strong tips, about 6 mm ($\frac{1}{4}$ in.) below a leaf joint. Clip off the lower leaves, leaving 2.5 cm (1 in.) or so of bare stem.*

2. *Dip the end of each cutting into a little hormone rooting powder, but not directly into the powder container. Fill 10 cm (4 in.) pots with damp coarse sand or vermiculite and pierce with three or four pencil-sized holes deep enough to cover the bare leaf joints. Insert a cutting into each hole, and firm the sand around it.*

3. *To provide both moisture and air circulation, place the potted cuttings in a slatted box, such as an orange crate, lined on the bottom with a 5 cm (2 in.) layer of damp moss peat or coarse sand. Cover the top of the box with a piece of glass or plastic, and set it outdoors in the shade. When new top growth appears, transplant the cuttings into individual pots filled with a proprietary potting compost, firming the soil around the new roots. Set the plants in the garden when you can see a network of new white roots in the soil ball.*

just below a point where a leaf stalk meets the stem. Strip the lowest leaves from the cutting and pinch off any buds or flowers; dip the bare end into hormone rooting powder (available at most garden centres) and insert each cutting about 2.5 centimetres (1 in.) deep in a pot or tray filled with a well-moistened rooting medium such as vermiculite, sphagnum moss or coarse sand. Enclose the pot or tray in a clear plastic bag or plastic cling film to conserve moisture, inserting plant labels or pencils in the medium to prop the plastic above the leaves. Tuck the open end of the plastic under the container, set this miniature greenhouse in a bright position out of direct sun, and make sure the rooting medium stays moist.

When the cuttings develop small new leaves, generally in two to four weeks, and their roots are about 2.5 centimetres (1 in.) long (gently pry one up to look), move them to separate pots filled with potting compost. After two or three weeks, tap one out of the pot to examine the root system. When the roots are strong enough, the herbs can be planted in the garden, at least in warmer climates. In cold regions they can be transplanted into individual pots filled with potting compost and left indoors over winter to be set in the garden the following spring.

Cuttings made from roots rather than stems can be taken from plants that send up new stems from spreading roots—verbascum, bergamot, horehound and perennial species of sage among others. Slice off the outer ends of a few roots with a sharp spade, discard the tapering thin ends of the roots and cut the remainders into sections 2.5 to 5 centimetres (1 to 2 in.) long. Lay these sections flat in a tray or box 2.5 centimetres (1 in.) or so apart on top of 7.5 centimetres (3 in.) of coarse sand or light garden soil, then cover them with 12 millimetres ($\frac{1}{2}$ in.) of the growing medium and water them thoroughly.

In cooler regions, root cuttings are best taken in the autumn and stored in the same growing medium on a cool verandah or in a cold frame outdoors until they send up shoots in spring and can be planted in the garden. In warmer climates, the tray or box can simply be covered with plastic and set outdoors out of direct sun; when new growth appears, the covering should be removed. When the new plants are 5 to 7.5 centimetres (2 to 3 in.) high, they are ready for the garden.

For shrubby perennial herbs like jasmine and rose, whose long, flexible stems sometimes droop along the ground, the layering method of starting new plants is convenient. In frost-prone areas this technique is best used in early spring to give the new plants time to establish themselves in the garden before autumn frost. Bend a stem down so it touches the ground about 30 centimetres (1 ft) from its tip. At this point scrape the lower bark surface with a knife if the stem is slender; in a thicker stem make a slanting cut part-way through the underside and wedge the cut open with a matchstick. Dust the exposed surface with hormone rooting powder, then bend the treated section down into a shallow, dish-shaped hole lined with a mixture of equal parts of soil, moss peat and coarse sand. Pin the section down with a loop of wire and bury it in more soil mixture, leaving about 15 centimetres (6 in.) of the stem tip protruding. Soak the buried section with water and put a stone on top to hold and mark the stem. Nourished by the parent plant, it may sprout roots of its own in as little as six weeks.

When the roots are established, as indicated by new growth on the exposed tip, cut the stem from its parent just below the ball of soil formed by the new roots. Transplant the new herb to a place of its own in the garden.

ROUTINE MAINTENANCE

To get the most from your herb garden, practise a few simple procedures to prolong the life of existing plants. Unless you find the flowers particularly decorative, pinch off the flower buds of basil, summer savory and other annuals and biennials; disbudding will delay their blossoming and enable you to harvest fresh leaves much longer through the summer. It is also advisable to remove the flower buds from the perennial chives.

To keep perennial herbs healthy through the winter, they should be given special attention in autumn. When the leaves of plants such as hyssop and chives have withered, cut old stalks to the ground. In cold regions, move tender evergreen perennials, such as rosemary and bay, inside before the frosts arrive.

WINTER PROTECTION

After the ground has frozen hard—and not before—guard perennial beds against premature thaws. They will be much better off if they remain frozen all winter long and are not subjected to alternate thawing and freezing, which can push plants out of the ground and cause serious damage to the roots. This protection is provided by a winter mulch; like a summer mulch, it is a blanket against the sun—to keep plants cold, not warm. It must be light and porous enough to allow air to penetrate, yet thick enough to shade and insulate the soil.

A winter mulch can be made of criss-crossed evergreen branches such as those left over from Christmas trees, or of a thick blanket of bracken, pine needles or straw. Spread it in a 10 to 15 centimetre (4 to 6 in.) layer over your perennial herb beds. Remove the mulch when the first new shoots of your herbs come up to greet the warmth of another spring.

Displays of beauty from utilitarian plants

Herb gardens started out as—and in most places still are—humbly practical affairs: small plots close by the kitchen door for the prudent housewife to reach into when she needed sprigs to flavour her stews or treat her family's ills. But in the 16th century these once-prosaic gardens became high fashion. Noblemen ordered the construction of conceits like knot gardens (*right*), in which the utilitarian herbs were planted and pruned in elaborate patterns. Although few people bother with such extravagances today, herbs are gaining renewed popularity, and modern gardeners find both traditional and innovative ways of using them decoratively.

To be a success, a herb garden must take into account the way herbs are used as well as their special physical qualities. Few bear spectacular blossoms. Yet the very lack of ostentatious flowers gives prominence to the subtle variations of the colour, texture and shape of their foliage. Equally important are their growth habits. Many herbs are obstinately unruly, leading gardeners to impose order on the wilful plants by laying them out in contained geometric designs.

Most experts recommend that a herb garden should be enclosed, if only by a low hedge. Besides providing shelter from the wind, an enclosure lends a formal structure to the garden. A central focal point—a special plant, a garden ornament, a small pool or a sundial—serves the same purpose. Given these design elements, a patterned layout of planting beds seems both natural and logical. For ease in tending and harvesting, the beds are often raised. This arrangement also improves drainage—a necessity for most herbs—and allows greater flexibility.

In many gardens the plants themselves are divided into beds according to leaf colour, height, use or growing habits. But gardeners seeking a more informal look plant their beds with a mixture of herbs and create visual unity with edgings of bricks or of a single perennial herb. Paths between beds help to contain the herbs while allowing access to the garden. Used together or singly, in small scale or large, these ideas lead to a herb garden that is tidy and attractive all the year round.

A knot garden at the Brooklyn Botanic Garden displays herbs simulating intertwined ribbons.

Common herbs uncommonly employed

A low dense hedge of grey-green cotton lavender outlines the edge of a large swimming pool. This linear herb garden not only perfumes the air but serves as a barrier, protecting the pool from drifting leaves carried by the wind from the adjacent lawn. To encourage bushy growth, the hedge must be clipped hard twice a year—in early spring and midsummer—with the odd trim in between.

The family dog and a "topiary" bird—created by shaping two myrtle bushes—confront each other on a lush green lawn. The owner shaped the bird from a piece of heavy galvanized wire staked between two container-grown plants (they must be taken indoors in winter). As branches grew, supported by wire, they were bent to form the tail, then the back and head and finally trimmed into the bird shape.

42

Myrtle corkscrews, sculpted by the topiarist who created the bird opposite, are made from bushes supported by stakes.

An order established by geometry

Angular beds edged in brick and raised above a background of white gravel paths establish and maintain the pattern of this terraced herb garden. On the upper level, triangular beds of yarrow, lady's mantle, sorrel and rosemary are set off by a large rectangular bed devoted entirely to mint. The round bed on the lower level contains lemon thyme, while lavender and germander fill the two wedges in front of the bench. The two tall-growing herbs that tower above all the others are mullein.

A brick-edged wheel, 4.5 metres (15 ft) across, is divided into wedges, each with its own environment, dry or moist, acid or alkaline. One, lower right, contains woad, madder and Nepal cinquefoil—all ancient dye plants suited to a dry, mild climate.

Breeze-blocks form the individual beds in this bushy, green herb garden. The centre bed has mounds of grey cotton lavender surrounded by germander and framed at the edge by two species of thyme. The one touch of red (far right) is flowering bergamot.

Two adjoining rectangular beds, raised on concrete footings and edged with local limestone, frame this herb garden. Slate benches built into the bed invite you to sit— a particularly pleasant idea for a garden devoted to fragrant herbs. Among its plantings are five kinds of thyme, two of sage and two clumps of lavender in full bloom. The spiky flowers at the rear of the first bed are foxgloves; the fragile blooms in the foreground of the second bed are horehound.

Into a tiny herb garden (left) the owner has incorporated such culinary or scented herbs as rosemary, lavender, artemisia, thyme, parsley, winter savory and horseradish, plus a few non-herbs such as the white shasta daisies and the pear tree.

A weathered wooden fence hems in a cornucopia of herbs outside an old farmhouse (above). Enclosed in a compact, accessible space are some 16 culinary herbs from angelica to thyme, along with a wide border of lavender and wormwood.

At the edge of a terrace, and overlooked by the living-room windows, this colourful herb garden was designed for year-round viewing. It is enclosed by a low brick wall, and the flagstone paths that meander through it are bordered with woolly lamb's ears, a herb that keeps its silvery foliage all winter. So do the dark green dwarf box plants that punctuate the garden at intervals. Along with herbs such as hyssop, thyme, sage, lavender and lady's mantle are a few non-herbs —begonias, dwarf barberry, tree paeony—for added interest.

The essential pathways

A wide gravel path edged with cedar boards gives easy access to a coastal herb garden. The plot is 6 metres (20 ft) square, surrounded on three sides with a post-and-rail fence and on the fourth side by bricks and a low hedge of lavender. Included in this mixture of annual and perennial herbs are some in pots that must overwinter indoors.

Wood chips cover two intersecting paths that cut through a broad expanse of woodruff. Woodruff, the traditional flavouring for May wine, is one of the few herbs that grows in the shade. Here it is used as an attractive ground cover under trees. The tidy paths are appropriate to the woodland setting and allow strollers to enjoy the plant's glossy leaves and tiny, star-shaped flowers at close range.

A broad grassy path edged in
brick bisects this varied herb
garden. The bricks, which separate
the path from the flower beds, also
disguise an even more effective
boundary. Beneath them lies a
1 metre (3 ft) deep trench, filled
with concrete to curb aggressive
roots. The herbs in the garden
include ornamental chives (front,
left) and, midway down the right
border, a clump of flowering basil.

Brick paths weave through a
rambling herb and flower garden
set in the middle of the countryside,
bringing a sense of order to an
informal design. Rosemary,
savory, sage, thyme, betony and
agrimony are just a few of the
herbs that intermingle with
delphiniums, moss roses, yarrow,
a quince tree and a pear tree. The
flowering border is of yellow
chamomile and orange marigolds.

Mirrors of the past

Four gates in a prim picket fence open into a large herb garden at Pennsbury, the restoration of William Penn's home near Morrisville, Pennsylvania. Penn, like many prudent colonists, grew his own herbs for household use—his first wife's recipe collection contains many references to them. The exact composition and location of Penn's garden have been lost, but this reconstruction, typical of 17th-century herb gardens, is thought to be much like his. Among the luxuriant plantings in the foreground are plots of tarragon, left, with horehound behind it; rue in the centre; and a clump of basil in full flower, right, behind dark green hyssop.

An early 18th-century limestone wall and a sculptured yew hedge enclose the herb garden at Cranborne Manor in Dorset (right) re-created by its present owner, Lady Salisbury, on what is thought to be the site of the manor's original 13th-century herb garden. Between 150 and 200 varieties of herbs are grown in the garden, including scented, culinary and medicinal herbs, among them a number of very old species, such as pennyroyal and motherwort. There are also 15 to 20 kinds of thyme, as well as many marjorams, sages and mints.

A garden
on the
window sill

The modern flat of a young computer programmer I know is an island of aromatic greenery in a sea of sterile concrete. Outside her windows is the city, indoors are pots, baskets and trays of growing herbs. In the living room a sweet olive, its stems laden with tiny chartreuse blooms, blends its fragrance with that of a snowy jasmine. In the kitchen this accomplished gardener snips sprigs of orange mint and thyme to add to celery leaves in a *bouquet garni* which she drops into a steaming saucepan of fresh green pea soup, transforming it from a plebeian to an epicurean dish. She grows herbs not just for their looks and aroma but for the extra flavour only freshly cut seasonings can give; anyone who dines at her table can tell the difference.

The profusion of plants, bushy and vigorous, thriving in that environment so distant from a garden suggests that herbs grow readily indoors. And so they do if, like my young friend, you know how to encourage them.

Some experienced gardeners will tell you that growing herbs indoors is child's play, and, in view of all the herb-growing kits on the market and the number of pots to be seen flourishing on kitchen window sills, you might take them at their word. But other gardeners, equally skilled, will tell you that herbs are the most recalcitrant of house plants. Both are partly right.

A comfortably large number of plants classified as herbs—including such culinary favourites as basil, bay, parsley and tarragon, and such tropical, sub-tropical and desert plants as scented geraniums, jasmine, sweet olive and aloe—grow readily indoors. But, like all plants, their demands must be met if they are to prosper. Most of them need at least five hours of direct sunlight a day, night temperatures under 15°C (60°F), good drainage, and high humidity—such as you get in a steamy kitchen, for instance. Given these conditions, they will reward you with a constant supply of flavourings and unusual greenery.

Safe from frost and handy for snipping, bushy thyme, broad-leaved basil and tall-growing sage thrive in one pot on a sunny window sill beside a pot of peppermint geranium. Nearby hang stalks of dried dill.

Many people who live in flats without gardens enjoy having a pot or two of each of their favourite herbs indoors all year round. Outdoor gardeners in cold regions often bring some herbs indoors in the autumn so that they can continue to harvest them through the winter, particularly herbs such as chives and parsley that taste so much better fresh than frozen or dried. Or they may move in tender shrubby herbs like rosemary, sweet bay and lemon verbena that would not survive hard frosts. Indoor herb gardening also provides a chance to try plants that in cold northern areas will prosper only in controlled conditions of warmth and moisture.

In selecting herbs to grow indoors, it is as well to follow a few rules. The first involves size. Most herbs grow smaller indoors because they get less than ideal light, temperature and room for their roots. Nevertheless, unless you have a great deal of space, you will probably want to avoid large plants like angelica, which grows 1.5 metres (5 ft) tall or more in the garden and half that size indoors. Smaller and more compact herbs such as sweet marjoram, thyme, parsley, winter savory and

HERBS THAT HANG

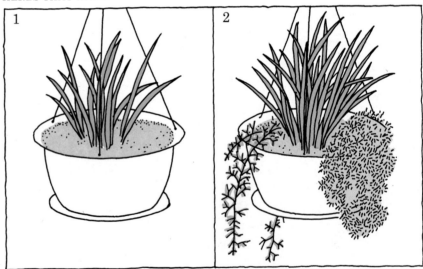

Select a plastic hanging pot that is equipped with an attached saucer to prevent dripping. Fill the pot with a proprietary potting compost and plant upright-growing herbs such as chives, basil or parsley in the centre. Start with well-rooted plants so that the ultimate space requirements for the full-grown root balls can be properly gauged.

Choose prostrate or cascading herbs such as lemon verbena, trailing rosemary, creeping thyme or nasturtium to plant around the outer edge of the garden. Hang the pot in a sunny window, and snip off ends of the herbs frequently to keep the foliage growing abundantly and to control the size and shape of the separate plants.

chives not only allow you to have more plants and greater variety, but they blend better with the smaller scale of indoor surroundings. Few houses or flats have space for plants like anise, coriander and caraway that are grown primarily for their seeds; to get enough seeds to be practical you would need several of each. Finally, some herbs simply are not suited to indoor growing—horseradish, orris root and marsh mallow among them —and unless you like challenges you will give them low priority.

The herbs you select to grow indoors are propagated in the same way as those raised in the garden. Plants that can be grown easily from seed—basil, dill, lavender, nasturtium and parsley, for example—can be sown in pots 7.5 to 15 centimetres (3 to 6 in.) in diameter any time in late summer. Start the seedlings outside if you have a place to do so, preferably six to 10 weeks before the first autumn frosts are expected, so that they will be growing vigorously when they have to face the adjustment of being moved inside. Sow three or four seeds in each pot, keep them barely moist and in a shady spot until they germinate, then move them into sunlight. When the seedlings are about 2.5 centimetres (1 in.) tall, remove all but the healthiest-looking one in each pot. Move the pots inside before the first frost is expected.

Perennials such as thyme, chives and lemon balm can be potted up from plants growing in the garden or bought from a nursery in late summer. If you are taking plants from the garden, dig up the entire plant at least a month before expected frosts. You can divide a large plant into several of more manageable size (Chapter 2). Set each plant into a pot that is about 2.5 centimetres (1 in.) larger than the ball of soil around the roots. Usually a pot 10 or 12.5 centimetres (4 or 5 in.) in diameter will suffice. Cut back one third to a half of the top growth to compensate for roots damaged in digging, keep the plants in shade for a week or 10 days to give them a chance to recover, then gradually move them into full sun until it is time to take them indoors. Cut off mature foliage at soil level to encourage vigorous new growth. Plants can also be started by means of stem cuttings, root cuttings or layering, as described in Chapter 2.

When buying plants, look for stocky, bushy ones with plenty of rich green (not pale or brown-edged) lower leaves. Check the soil surface in the pot and the drainage hole in the bottom; if roots are beginning to protrude either above or below, the plant may need repotting, a job you should do before bringing it indoors. It is also a good idea to check the stems and undersides of leaves for insect infestations. Although herbs

PLANT TOWER FOR A PATIO

1. *To grow herbs in a small area such as a patio, construct a cylindrical herb tower from a 1.2 metre (4 ft) wide piece of 7.5 cm (3 in.) welded wire mesh cut 1.5 metres (5 ft) long. Do not use chicken wire—the small openings make planting difficult.*

2. *Position the mesh rectangle so that the long sides are parallel to the floor, and bend it into a cylinder. Twist the cut ends of wire around a vertical section of the mesh to hold the structure together, turning tips inwards.*

3. *Line the cylinder with waterproof roofing felt. For a movable tower, mount it on a 60 cm (2 ft) square of 2 cm (¾ in.), exterior plywood fitted with castors. For a stationary one, put lining material under it. Fill the cylinder with potting compost.*

4. *Mark squares for planting holes, staggering them so that one is not directly beneath another. Leave enough closed squares to support the soil. Cut the lining material at the marked squares.*

5. *Select the herbs you wish to plant. Position upright herbs such as chives or basil at the top; spreading ones, such as mint, and moisture-loving plants at the bottom. Set the plants at a slight angle in the cut-out holes, or plant seeds, three or four to a hole, at a depth three times their diameter.*

6. *When the tower is planted, water it thoroughly from the top. Make sure it is kept constantly moist, watering it daily in dry weather, or using a hose attachment that drips water.*

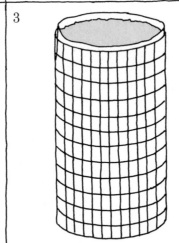

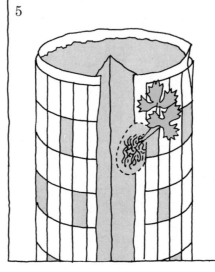

are relatively pest free, they sometimes pick up pests from other plants; watch out for the speckled discoloration that indicates the presence of tiny red spider mites, or the wispy clouds of whiteflies, which may flutter away like animated snowflakes when you shake the plant. Whether you buy a plant or move one in from the garden, put it in quarantine for a couple of weeks, away from other plants, and recheck to make sure it is not bringing in any insects that might set off an epidemic among your other house plants.

If you do find that insects have taken up residence, turn the plant upside down, holding it in its pot, and swish its leaves around in a bucket of tepid soapy water (use mild soap, not a detergent). If necessary, add a pesticide such as malathion or diazinon to the water. Follow label instructions and wear rubber gloves. Scale insects, sometimes visible on the stems and backs of the leaves of such plants as sweet bay, can be scrubbed off with an old toothbrush after they have been killed by the insecticide. If the infestation persists, spray the plant outdoors: it can be brought indoors after its leaves have dried. In this way the chemicals used to control the pests will not harm human beings or pets. If this treatment fails, it is best to discard the plant.

CHOOSING A CONTAINER

To hold your indoor herbs, a myriad of tubs, boxes and hanging baskets are available, but the oldest and in many ways still the most versatile container is the familiar flower pot. Old-fashioned clay pots do very well; excess water evaporates readily through their porous walls, their weight makes them harder to tip over accidentally, and their colour will blend into almost any decorating scheme. In time, the moisture coming through the sides may leave a deposit of whitish fertilizer salts or encourage the growth of splotches of green algae; encrusted pots can be scrubbed clean with soapy water. Soak dry clay pots in water for several hours before using; otherwise they may absorb soil moisture, robbing the plants.

Where weight is a consideration, as in small hanging gardens of herbs (*page 56*) or a large container for a bay or orange tree that you want to move around, plastic pots are particularly useful. Their lack of porosity can also be a convenience for many herbs: since they do not transpire moisture through their sides, their contents need to be watered only one third as often as plants in clay pots. But they also increase the danger of drowning a plant by waterlogging its roots—a fate to which many herbs, with their need for good drainage, are very susceptible. Plastic pots are generally safe for herbs that

59

The perfumed geraniums

Unlike the ubiquitous window-box geranium, loved for its profusion of blooms, the scented geranium is prized for its aromatic, unusually shaped foliage (although a few, such as 'Clorinda', below, bear striking flowers). Some smell of roses; others, such as 'Snowflake' (*far right*), of rose mixed with mint or lemon. Geraniums that smell of limes, strawberries and oranges are other entries in this garden of 200 or so olfactory delights. The leaves may be narrow and fern-like (*P. denticulatum* 'Filicifolium', *right*) or broad as saucers (*P. tomentosum, far right*) in shades of green or speckled or rimmed with other colours. To compound their complexity, scented geraniums are actually pelargoniums, a subgroup of the geranium family.

P. X DOMESTICUM 'CLORINDA'
Large vividly coloured flowers, eucalyptus scent

P. CRISPUM 'VARIEGATUM'
"Gooseberry" geranium, lemon scent

P. GRAVEOLENS
Original rose-scented geranium

P. DENTICULATUM 'FILICIFOLIUM'
Fern-like leaves, intense pine aroma

P. TOMENTOSUM
Headiest of the peppermint scents

P. CAPITATUM 'SNOWFLAKE'
White-speckled leaves, mint-rose scent

P. GRAVEOLENS 'VARIEGATUM'
White-edged leaves, mint-rose aroma

61

can tolerate dampness, such as mints and sweet woodruff. And, if you use a light, sandy soil mixture and avoid overwatering, they can be used for others as well.

No matter what material it is made of, any pot should have a drainage hole or holes in the bottom to prevent water from collecting inside, and a saucer or tray underneath to collect the run-off, preferably with a layer of pebbles to keep the drainage hole above the water. The riskiest containers are the glazed urns that have no drainage holes at all; but you can set a second, slightly smaller pot containing the plant inside such an urn, propping it up on a brick or a layer of pebbles.

Indoor-grown herbs require a carefully selected growing mixture. Ordinary garden soil may harbour insect eggs and weed seeds; furthermore, it is generally too heavy with clay to provide sufficient drainage around the confined roots of a potted herb. Garden soil can be sterilized in a kitchen oven, then mixed with additives to lighten it, but most indoor gardeners buy packaged potting compost, which is already sterilized and mixed with lightening agents and nutrients. Potting compost sold for house plants can generally be used as it comes. But, if good drainage is especially important, as with aloe or houseleek, lighten the mixture with one part sand or vermiculite to three parts compost. For a tropical plant such as jasmine, use a mixture with a high organic content like that sold for African violets.

ENSURING DRAINAGE   To ensure proper drainage and prevent clogging, place a crock from an old broken clay pot, convex side up, over the hole or holes or put a 12 millimetre ($\frac{1}{2}$ in.) layer of small pebbles in the bottom of a small or medium-size pot; if the pot is 15 centimetres (6 in.) or more in diameter, use a layer up to 2.5 centimetres (1 in.) deep. Add enough potting mixture to ensure that the plant will sit with the top of its soil ball 12 millimetres ($\frac{1}{2}$ in.) below the top of the pot; in large pots—20 centimetres (8 in.) or more—it should be 2.5 centimetres (1 in.) below.

If you are removing a plant from its temporary nursery container, or repotting one that has outgrown its pot, water it thoroughly half an hour ahead of time so that it will slip out of the pot easily with the soil ball clinging around its roots. If the roots are visible and crowded, growing round and round the soil ball like spaghetti, move the plant to a larger pot; or hose the roots to remove outside soil and then shave off the matted outer roots with a sharp knife. Trim an equal amount off the bottom; then, to keep the plant in balance, trim a roughly proportionate amount of top growth.

Set the plant in the pot you have prepared and hold it

upright as you fill in with soil mixture around the sides, poking it down with fingers or a stick to make sure no air pockets remain. When you have filled the pot level with the top of the soil ball, press down with both thumbs round the edge to firm the soil mixture into place; then water the plant until water seeps out of the drainage hole.

Once you have potted your herbs properly, you are ready to move them indoors to where they will grow best. For the majority of herbs, this means a place where they will get as much sun as possible, and in most parts of Europe that usually means on a south-facing window sill. The next best choice is a window facing east or west, though hot afternoon sun pouring in the latter for several hours a day may require you to keep watch for wilting, and either move sensitive plants away from the glass or hang a net curtain to filter the rays. A few shade-tolerant species such as mint and sweet woodruff will do reasonably well in a north window with bright light.

If you lack windows with the proper exposure, you can still grow herbs indoors—under artificial light. Many gardeners prefer this method because it gives them a more reliable source than natural light and results in a healthy, bushy symmetry that

REPOTTING TO CONTROL GROWTH

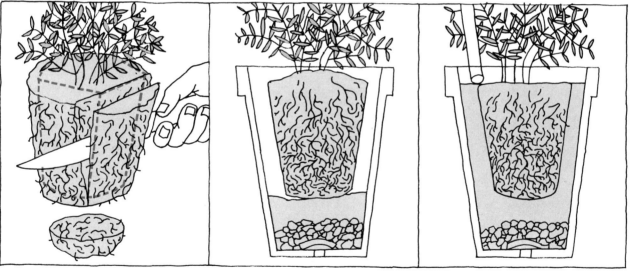

Because the roots of many herbs grow rapidly into tangled masses, frequent pruning and repotting are necessary. Knock the plant out of the pot and, with a sharp knife, cut one third off the root ball. Then trim the same amount of top growth.

Select a pot 2.5 cm (1 in.) larger in diameter. Add 2.5 cm (1 in.) of pebbles and a crock over the hole to ensure good drainage. Cover with potting compost so that the top of the root ball is about 2.5 cm (1 in.) below the pot's rim.

Add more soil around the root ball, using a stick or dibber to tamp the soil firmly and eliminate air pockets. Add soil as necessary. Water the plant thoroughly; then place it in the shade for a few days until it becomes acclimatized.

USING ARTIFICIAL LIGHT
Create a kitchen herb garden by mounting a two-tube fluorescent fixture under a kitchen cabinet. Insert one "cool" and one "warm" white 20-watt, 60 cm (2 ft) tube. To provide humidity, place a 2.5 cm (1 in.) layer of pebbles in a waterproof tray. Place potted plants on the tray, varying their distance from the light source to suit their size by setting them on bricks, inverted flower pots or pieces of wood; the top leaves should be 10 to 15 cm (4 to 6 in.) from the tubes. Keep the lights on for 14 to 16 hours a day.

WATERING REQUIREMENTS

window-sill plants sometimes do not have. To provide the full spectrum of light wavelengths that plants require, either use the special fluorescent tubes made for this purpose or combine two ordinary tubes, one labelled "cool white" and the other "warm white". If necessary, set the potted plants on bricks or inverted pots so that the tubes are an optimum 10 to 15 centimetres (4 to 6 in.) above the top leaves of the plants. Keep the lights on for 14 to 16 hours a day if they are the sole light source, or use them for a few hours each day to supplement natural light.

As important as sufficient light, are proper temperature, which should be fairly low (especially at night), and humidity, which should be relatively high. Most homes are far too hot and dry in winter for plants, even those herbs that come from hot, dry Mediterranean climates. During the day, the situation is rarely critical; many herbs will tolerate temperatures that rise to 21°C (70°F) and higher. But they have evolved to require a rest in the coolness of the outdoor night, when the usual temperature during the growing season is 15°C (60°F) or less. The best way to ensure this is to turn the thermostat down to 15°C (60°F) at night. During fuel shortages many people who lowered their thermostats as a conservation measure discovered that their house plants flourished as never before. Alternatively, keep the plants in an enclosed, unheated (but not freezing) sun porch or in a spare room where the temperature is kept lower.

Indoor atmosphere may stagnate in winter, so give the plants some fresh air by opening a window for half an hour or so once a day. But make sure they are not exposed to a direct blast of icy air; choose a window well away from the plants.

Many windows that are best for maximum natural light are the worst for heat since they are positioned directly above radiators or warm-air vents. The heat can make the air around such a window even drier than that in the rest of the house. The way to solve both problems is to deflect the heat away from the pots and simultaneously humidify the air around the leaves. Group the pots in trays that will partially shield them from hot air and also serve as simple humidifiers. Raise the pots by covering the trays with a 2.5 centimetre (1 in.) layer of pebbles. Keep the water level just below the bottoms of the pots so the soil cannot draw up moisture to waterlog the roots. The evaporating moisture will help to keep the relative humidity around the leaves at a beneficial 40 to 60 per cent.

While herbs benefit from humidity around their leaves, special care must be taken that they do not get too much round their roots, whether they are set in humidity trays or not. Overwatering is the principal threat to herbs indoors, just as its concomitant, poor drainage, is the major villain outdoors.

The best time to water is in the morning so that plants can use the moisture and nutrients in the soil during the daylight hours and so that any excess moisture can evaporate readily. Water applied in the afternoon or evening tends to stand around the roots and stems overnight, inviting fungus and rot. In a warm room, plants sometimes cannot take up cold water as rapidly as they lose moisture through their leaves, so they may wilt even if the soil feels moist. To prevent this and to aid the general health of your plants, always use tepid water. To water, fill the space at the top of the pot with water up to the rim, and repeat if necessary until water begins to seep out through the bottom drainage hole: check later to make sure the plants are not standing in excess water.

If a plant has gone longer than usual between waterings, and dusty soil or wilting leaves indicate that it is bone dry, submerge the whole pot in a sink or bucket of tepid water. Soak it until the air bubbles stop rising from the soil surface, then set it aside to drain for about 20 minutes. Many indoor herb gardeners immerse their plants every two or three weeks, and use the opportunity to wash dust from the leaves.

FERTILIZER REQUIREMENTS

With the proper soil mixture, indoor conditions and watering, your herbs will need only a little fertilizer at well-spaced intervals to supply their needs, especially if they receive less than optimum light. Most 5:10:5 fertilizers designed for house plants will do. Use the house-plant fertilizer mixed at half the recommended strength. Wait two or three weeks before feeding a newly potted plant to give it time to re-establish its root system so that it can take up the nourishment, and do not feed any plant without watering it first, lest the concentrated chemicals burn the tender roots. Most herbs benefit from a light feeding in the autumn, after they have adjusted to conditions indoors. From late autumn through to early winter they will not get enough sunlight to warrant any feeding, but they can be fertilized again from late winter or early spring. From spring to autumn, feed about half as often as the package suggests.

By the time warm weather arrives in spring, your herbs will be ready to spend an increasing amount of time outdoors. Set them on the sill of an open window or on a terrace, bringing them in on nights when temperatures threaten to drop below 4°C (40°F). If a plant has become weak and spindly and does not respond to this treatment, take a cutting to start a new plant and throw the old one away.

Making the most of the harvest

Herb gardening brings extra dividends. Beyond the pleasures of planting and watching the herbs grow are the delights of the harvest. Most herbs can be used fresh or preserved in various ways for later enjoyment. In either form, their uses are nearly endless, ranging from decorative, scented mixtures to drink flavourings, tasty herb vinegars, butters and salts. Some people grow herbs to dry for winter bouquets, or for use in potpourris. Others add them to their palette of natural vegetable dyes. Still others—since old beliefs die slowly—attribute strange powers to these ancient plants. One gardener of my acquaintance, who grows several hundred kinds of herbs at her farm, recalls an occasion when she was asked for assistance by a distraught man who said he had lost his best friend.

"Is he dead?" the herb gardener asked.

"No, but he is so angry he won't speak to me," was the answer. He wanted a herb that would solve his problem.

Sifting through her memory of ancient lore, the herb gardener (who prefers to remain anonymous because she does not believe in such occult remedies) suggested slipping the angry one something with cumin seed in it, perhaps a tempting piece of home-made cake. The next time she saw the man, she anxiously asked him what had happened.

"Oh, it worked like a charm," he replied. "You certainly know your herbs!"

Although the average gardener is more likely to use herbs in cooking than in witchcraft, he would be well advised to follow certain traditional practices. These culinary techniques depend, first of all, not only on the plant involved but on whether its leaves are to be used fresh or are to be preserved. For immediate use, pick leaves at any time before the plants bloom—the sooner the better in the case of those, such as borage, burnet or nasturtium, that are to be eaten in salads.

In a table-top potpourri, whole roses, a rosebud (lower left) and a eucalyptus seed pod (centre left) rest among petals and leaves of roses, violas, eucalyptus, bay, artemisia and scented geraniums.

Use a sharp pair of scissors, a knife or, on softer stems, your fingernails, to snip off a sprig or two from the tops of the plants, just above the next set of leaves lower down the stalk. This process, which gardeners call pinching back, not only provides you with tender young leaves when you need them, but will improve the plant's health and appearance by stimulating it to put out additional fresh, bushy growth. Watch also for flower buds forming on annuals such as basil or on perennials such as chives or the tender marjoram; if you pinch them off before they bloom, the plants will reward you by continuing to produce edible leaves instead of flowering and becoming tough as the seeds are set. To perpetuate annuals without having to buy a new supply of seed each year, let one or two of each kind of plant flower and go to seed naturally. You can collect the seeds and save them for later planting, but most annual herbs reseed themselves—if you let their seeds fall to the ground, new plants will come up the following spring.

HARVESTING FROM CLUMPS Because of a special way of growing, certain herbs require a somewhat different harvesting technique. Among these are plants such as chives, lovage and parsley, which send up clumps of leaves or grass-like spears directly from their roots. Do not snip off the tops, giving the plant a "haircut", because repeated harvesting in this way will shear it progressively closer to the ground. This not only reduces the leaves to unsightly, yellow-tipped stubble but also prevents them from manufacturing the food supply to be stored in the roots over the winter so that the plants will have enough energy to regenerate vigorously the following spring. Instead, cut whole spears from the outside of the clump, snipping them off just above ground level. This method will provide seasoning for eggs, cold soups or salads without affecting the looks or wellbeing of the plants.

PICKING LEAVES TO KEEP While the young leaves of most culinary herbs can be snipped at any time if they are to be used fresh, those meant to be preserved for future use, either by drying or freezing, should be harvested at special periods of growth. A few—parsley, lovage, winter savory and burnet—should be cut early while leaves are still tender. But most leaves are best collected for preservation just as the plants come into bloom. It is immediately before flowering that most plants contain the maximum amount of fragrant oils in their thousands of tiny leaf glands, and since some of the oil is bound to be lost in the preserving process it is as well to start with leaves that are at their best.

The ideal time of day to harvest any herb for preservation is

CUTTING CHIVES AND PARSLEY
When you pick small amounts of grassy herbs such as chives, or those that send up stalks directly from the ground, such as parsley and lovage, use a special harvesting technique. Do not shear off the tops of the stalks, for the plants will then look unattractively stubby; instead, cut off individual stalks from the outside edges of the plants, just above ground level. This method not only preserves the shapes of the plants but encourages the growth of new stalks. Harvested in this way the stalks will be tender right down to the ground.

early on a sunny morning, just after the dew has evaporated. Later in the day, the sun's heat may release some of the oils.

When cutting for preservation, it is important not only to select the right harvesting time but also to use an appropriate picking method. Cut off annuals far enough above the ground so that some leafy growth remains; in the case of early-blooming species, such as chervil and summer savory, this method will leave enough of the plant to produce new growth for a second harvest later. With shrubby tender herbs, such as rosemary and sweet marjoram, trim a few centimetres off the tip of each branch as the herbs are needed. Trimming the plants in this way will encourage new growth while providing fresh leaves for the cooking pot.

Keep the cut stems of different herbs in separate bunches, and wrap them loosely in newspaper or paper bags. Bring the bunches in out of the sun as soon as possible, rinse off dirt, then spread each bunch on a table and remove any dead leaves. It is a good idea to label each batch so that you can keep track of it throughout the preserving process; as the leaves dry they will shrink, change colour and become far less recognizable so that it is all too easy to get them mixed up.

The problem of keeping varieties separate was solved in a different way in the 19th century by the Shakers, in the religious communes that were engaged in the commercial production of herbs during the American Civil War years. A member of one of these celibate groups, Marcia Bullard, described in these words the efficient means by which the Shakers harvested their herbs: "There were herbs of many kinds. Lobelia, pennyroyal, spearmint, peppermint, catnip, wintergreen, thoroughwort, sarsaparilla and dandelion grew wild in the surrounding fields. When it was time to gather them, an elderly brother would take a great wagonload of children, armed with tow sheets, to the pastures. Here they would pick the appointed herb—each one had its own day, that there might be no danger of mixing—and, when their sheets were full, drive solemnly back home again."

HANGING BUNCHES TO DRY In those days, as now, most leaf herbs were preserved simply by letting them dry out thoroughly and then storing them in airtight containers. An easy method for plants that have long stems and dry quickly—such as savory, sage, mint, marjoram and rosemary—is to arrange the cut ends in small bunches, fasten them together, then hang each bunch upside down indoors in a dry, well-ventilated place. To support the bunches, string a length of cord or suspend a rod horizontally from the ceiling, and spread a cloth or newspapers beneath the bunches to catch dried leaves that fall off. Do not hang the bunches against a wall, which would block air circulation and interfere with complete drying. To keep dust from settling on the leaves and to catch those that fall off, some herb gardeners hang each bunch of leaves inside a paper bag generously punched with ventilation holes on the sides; the bag is then suspended so that the herbs dry upside down.

In about two weeks, somewhat longer in humid weather, the suspended, quick-drying leaves should crackle to the touch. Take each bunch down carefully, spread it on a clean cloth and strip the leaves off the stems. Some foliage, such as the needles of rosemary, becomes hard and sharp, so you may want to protect your hands with gloves.

If you have placed the bunches in paper bags, shake each bag and listen for dried leaves falling to the bottom. When the foliage is dry and crumbly, roll the bag gently between your hands to remove most of the leaves from the stems, then empty the contents and pick off the remaining leaves.

Throw away the stems. They tend to retain some moisture and become mouldy in storage. If you like, keep some of the whole leaves in a separate jar to use for herb teas; the remaining whole or partly broken leaves can be stored as they are, or they can be crumbled between your hands or rubbed through a coarse sieve. The larger the pieces of leaves, the longer they will retain their flavour; however, the crumbled herb leaves concentrate more flavour in less volume and thus can be stored in less space, such as small airtight storage jars.

Leaves that dry more slowly, such as those of parsley, lovage and basil, should be plucked from their stems at the time of harvest. They can be spread on the floor of a warm, airy attic to dry. Or, to speed the process, spread them on baking sheets or muslin-covered trays and dry them in the lower part of an oven set at its lowest temperature, leaving the door ajar. Remove the leaves as soon as they are dry to the touch so that heat does not bake out the oils.

Many gardeners dry herbs in yet another way—on stacked horizontal trays that permit ample circulation of air. This method can be used for virtually any herb but is particularly suited to short-stemmed, wiry herbs, such as creeping varieties of thyme, that cannot readily be tied in bundles. It is also helpful with plants such as sweet bay, from which you may want to harvest only a few large leaves, and with lemon verbena, which should be harvested after the plant is moved indoors for the winter but before the leaves drop. For drying trays, use window screens with either wood or metal frames, or make special trays by joining lengths of light timber into frames over which cheesecloth or muslin is stapled. Put the trays in a dry place, out of direct sunlight, where they can remain undisturbed

HANGING HERBS WITH LONG STEMS

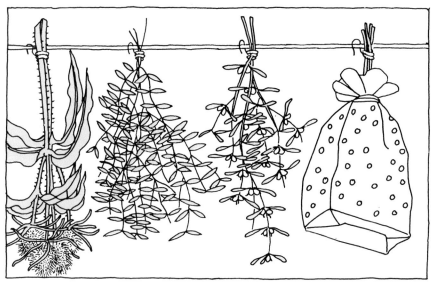

Cut herbs such as sage and mint just above ground level; then rinse the leaves in lukewarm water. Separate each kind into small bouquets held with rubber bands, which will contract as stems shrink. Use paper clips to hang the herbs in a dry and well-ventilated place such as a kitchen or attic. Where seed heads might drop off, enclose the bunches in perforated paper bags (above, right). Herbs should be dry in a week or two.

for several days and where air can circulate freely over, under and through them. Prop single trays on two chairs or, for larger harvests of herbs, either stack several one on top of the other separated by blocks, or make trays that stack together on their own legs (*drawings, page 74*).

COLLECTING SEEDS   The tray-drying method is also useful when preserving herbs grown for their flavourful seeds, among them dill, caraway, coriander, cumin and anise, as well as when collecting seeds to save for planting. As soon as the seed heads become dry and brown or grey, and the seeds themselves have lost their greenish colour and are about to drop, cut entire seed heads one at a time so that they fall into a cloth-lined basket or paper bag. Some gardeners keep a supply of labelled bags on hand and gradually accumulate seed heads until they have enough to process a substantial batch. Spread the seed heads on the drying trays and keep them in a dry, well-ventilated place for five or six days.

When the seed heads are thoroughly dry, rub them between your hands so that the seeds drop on to the trays, discard the stripped stems and gently shake each tray, blowing on it to winnow out the remaining chaff. Then stack the trays again so

HOW TO PICK AND DRY LEAVES

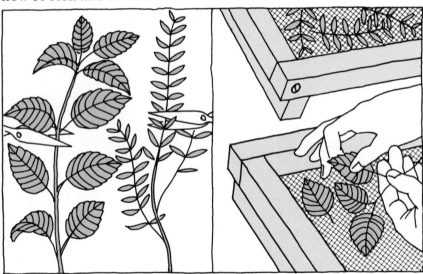

Just before the plant blooms—when its oils are heavily concentrated—cut off about a quarter of the top of large-leaved plants; remove sprigs of small-leaved ones. As the growing season ends, cut at ground level.

Rinse off any dirt. Strip large leaves from the stem, but keep sprigs intact. Lay leaves and sprigs, one layer deep and separated so that none touch, on drying trays (page 74). Dry until the leaves are crisp.

that the seeds can dry for another week or 10 days, occasionally shaking the trays in order to make sure that all the seed surfaces are equally exposed to the air.

After drying leaves or seeds, store them in airtight containers that will keep them dry, free of mould and at their flavourful best. You can use decorative glass spice jars or apothecary jars, so long as the tops provide good seals, or empty pill bottles or screw-top jam jars. Larger quantities can be sealed in glass preserving jars or coffee tins.

Glass shows off the leaves or seeds attractively and makes it easy to keep track of how much you have left. Perhaps more important, a transparent container makes it easy to check to see if moisture is condensing inside, critical during the first week or so after the herbs have been dried. If you see a mist of droplets forming inside the glass, you will know that the leaves or seeds still have some moisture in them and will soon become mouldy or rot if they are left in the container; promptly pour them out and dry them for another two or three days on a drying tray, or briefly in a cool oven, before returning them to storage.

COOL, SHADED STORAGE

To prolong the useful life of the dried herbs, their containers should be kept in a cool place. Glass jars should be kept out of direct sunlight, which makes the leaves fade and draws out the oils. Though such containers may be decorative with sunlight shining through them, do not put them in a kitchen window unless it is well shaded or faces north. And do not put any herb container on a shelf near a stove or other appliance that gives off heat. This is especially important for the seeds that you intend to plant; they are best stored in a cool, dark place to ensure the vitality of the seed embryos while in storage.

Label each container with the name of the herb it contains and note the date when the batch was packed. Though some seeds—for example, balm, borage and coriander—keep satisfactorily for several years, leaf herbs lose most of their flavour after six months or so and should be discarded and replaced.

TECHNIQUES FOR FREEZING

While the leaves of most culinary herbs can be dried for later use, many can be frozen with equal ease and sometimes with better results. Many gardener-cooks prefer this method, particularly for such delicately flavoured leaves as those of chives, basil, burnet, parsley, fennel and dill. Though many herbs wilt when they are frozen, and some, like basil, turn darker, their flavour will remain remarkably fresh even after a year in the freezer. Once the herbs have thawed, any leftovers should be discarded, not refrozen. It is a good idea to freeze herbs such as parsley and chives in ice-cube trays and then store the cubes in small plastic bags in the freezer; when you want to use them you simply pop a cube or two into the sauce or soup. But frozen herbs cannot be used to garnish dishes, even after thawing.

In the days before the home freezer was a common appliance, gardeners used to preserve delicate herbs in salt—placing sprigs between layers of salt in earthenware pots. The encrusted salt had to be washed off before the herbs could be used. Some cooks continue to use this method, but most people find it easier to store clean, fresh leaves in the freezer.

Like herbs that are to be dried, herbs to be frozen should be gathered on a sunny morning soon after the dew has disappeared; rinse off dirt, remove dead leaves and pat the sprigs dry on a

MAKING DRYING TRAYS

1. *Construct simple stacking trays for drying herbs from lengths of 5 by 5 cm (2 by 2 in.) timber and muslin. Size is optional, but for convenient handling the trays should be no smaller than 40 by 53 cm (1⅓ by 1¾ ft) and no larger than 60 by 90 cm (2 by 3 ft). Cut the framing sections and assemble with nails or screws. Sandpaper rough edges.*

2. *Cut the muslin to measure about 2.5 cm (1 in.) larger than the inside frame opening. Stretch the material across the frame; then attach it with staples or carpet tacks.*

3. *Cut two more pieces of wood for the spacers, the same length as the short ends of the frame. To make the trays easier to handle, set the spacers 12 mm (½ in.) in from the short ends of the frame.*

4. *When using the trays, save space by stacking the trays one on top of the other. The spacer pieces will leave 10 cm (4 in.) between the levels of muslin to allow air to circulate freely above and below them. (How the herbs should be arranged on each tray for proper drying is shown on page 72.)*

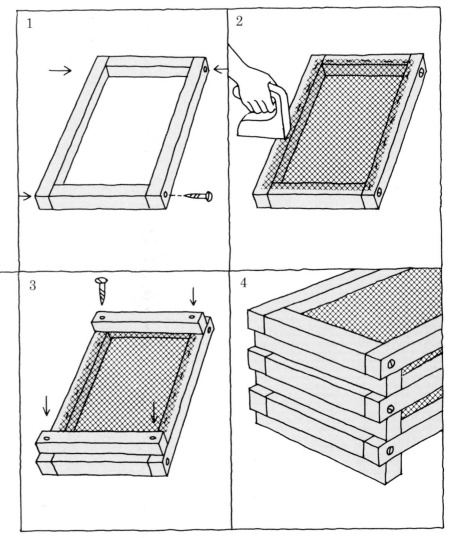

paper towel. Some people maintain that the flavour is best preserved by blanching the leaves in boiling water for a minute and then plunging them into iced water immediately. But other gardeners believe that herbs will last as long and taste even fresher if they are simply wrapped and frozen. Put small, convenient amounts in individual clear plastic bags and then clip a handful of bags together or put them in a larger freezer container, adding a label with the name of the herb and the date of freezing. This way you can remove individual bags with enough leaves for one dish without disturbing the rest of your supply.

You can also store separate servings of herb mixtures—parsley, chives and tarragon, for example—in small packets so you do not have to find and open several different bags each time you make a dish that calls for that combination. Put the leaves or sprigs into their packages whole; they will retain their flavour a little longer that way.

PACKAGING MIXTURES

Fresh, dried or frozen, the culinary herbs can be used in numerous ways, as the recipes in many of today's cookery books will attest. Not all cookery books, however, provide general guidelines for using herbs. Expert cooks say that herbs should be used sparingly, to bring out and enhance the natural flavour of a dish, perhaps to give it an unexpected touch, but rarely to dominate it. It is better to err on the side of caution when it comes to using pungent herbs such as rosemary, marjoram, garlic and sage; a little goes a long way, and too much can make people dislike a herb or the dish it is used in.

When experimenting with a new recipe, use a little less than the instructions call for; it is easy enough to add more of a herb to taste. Be especially careful when using dried herbs, which, despite the loss of some of their oils, are usually stronger than fresh ones if the same volume measures are compared. Their oils become concentrated as the leaves shrivel, crumble and lose moisture. As a general rule, $\frac{1}{4}$ teaspoon of a dried, finely powdered herb is roughly equivalent to $\frac{1}{2}$ teaspoon of dried and loosely crumbled leaves, and to $1\frac{1}{2}$ to 2 teaspoons of fresh chopped leaves. Frozen leaves may lose a little flavour, but they can be used in the amounts specified for fresh leaves. If you are trying out a recipe that is vague as to amounts, or if you are creating a recipe of your own, a safe rule of thumb is to use no more than $\frac{1}{4}$ teaspoon of a dried herb, or 1 teaspoon of a chopped fresh or frozen herb, to every four servings.

EXTRA FLAVOUR FROM DRYING

Every cook develops personal ideas about which herbs to use in which dishes, but certain herbs have proved good companions for certain foods—chives with eggs, basil with tomatoes, tarragon with chicken, mint with lamb, and so on. As you become more familiar with the distinctive tastes of specific herbs, you may want to try some variations of your own, but it is best to remember that extremely pungent herbs such as rosemary, sage and thyme are rarely used together because their competing flavours tend to clash.

Some herb mixtures, of course, are basics of good French cooking—for example, *fines herbes* and *bouquet garni*. The former are blends of compatible flavours, often used in egg and cheese dishes or sprinkled over casseroles or fish. Each blend usually includes one member of the allium family, such as chives, one member of the parsley family, such as curly or flat-leaved parsley or chervil, and one, two or even three others with distinctive flavours, such as tarragon, basil, sweet marjoram or thyme. A blend especially good with stews and soups is half lovage and half parsley. Blends of *fines herbes* can be made of chopped fresh or frozen leaves, or of dried leaves; to release their flavour at the right moment, they are usually sprinkled into a dish during the last few minutes of cooking, or over an omelette just before it is folded and served.

HOW TO SEPARATE THE SEEDS

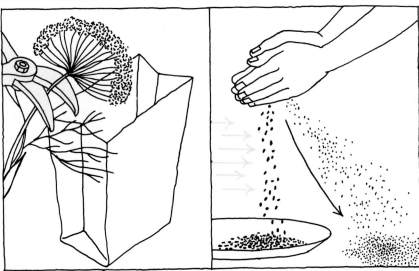

Pick the seeds of herbs such as dill, coriander, anise and caraway when capsules begin to open. Cut the stems a few centimetres below the seed heads, bending the stalks so seeds drop into a paper bag.

Hang the bag in a dry place for a week. Then set a large bowl in a light breeze and rub the heads between your hands; the breeze will blow the chaff aside while seeds fall into the bowl. Dry seeds and seal in jars.

A *bouquet garni* is a mixture of several herbs—fresh, frozen or dried—that is added to stocks, soups, stews and other dishes while they are cooking but is removed before the dish is served. A basic bouquet can be made by tying together three or four sprigs of parsley or chervil, a couple of sprigs of thyme, one bay leaf, and sometimes a celery leaf or two. The herb mixture can be wrapped in the green upper part of a couple of leek leaves for easy tying. Use light cotton string or heavy thread and leave several centimetres attached so that you can pull the bouquet out of the pot at the end of cooking. This combination is often varied or added to: a sprig of basil for tomatoes, one of marjoram or tarragon for poultry, one of rosemary for lamb or beef.

For a basic bouquet of dried herbs, mix 1 tablespoon of dried parsley or chervil with $\frac{1}{2}$ tablespoon of thyme leaves and half a bay leaf. Place this blend on a double thickness of muslin 7.5 centimetres (3 in.) square, gather up the sides and tie it with string or heavy thread to make a little bag, leaving a few centimetres of loose string for pulling the bag out of the pot.

Alone or in combinations, herbs can be used not only to season various cooked dishes but to add their flavours to vinegars, dressings, dips and drinks.

Herb vinegars can be made from virtually any culinary herb. Mint vinegar is good with lamb, ham or coleslaw; a dash of basil vinegar gives a glass of tomato juice or a tomato aspic an added tang; garlic vinegar with oil and a little pepper and salt makes a tasty French dressing. Some herbs add colour as well as special flavour: purple basil makes clear vinegar rich ruby red.

The simplest way to make herb vinegar is to place several sprigs of leaves (or a couple of garlic or shallot cloves) in a bottle with a non-metal top, fill it with white distilled vinegar and set it aside in a cool dark place for several weeks. If you use cider or wine vinegar, add herbs with strong flavours, such as tarragon, mint, bay or basil. To speed the process, crush the leaves or cloves, and heat the vinegar to just below boiling point before adding the herbs and bottling. Strain out the crushed residue after about 10 days and rebottle. Leave a few sprigs or blossoms floating in the bottles for decoration.

Herb butter—ordinary butter flavoured with different herbs or combinations like *fines herbes*—adds a marvellous flavour to hot French bread, and it is delicious when melted over grilled chops and steaks. Simply add finely chopped herbs to butter that has been allowed to warm to room temperature. For 100 grams ($\frac{1}{4}$ lb), use 4 tablespoons of fresh leaves or 2 tablespoons of dried leaves, though a tablespoon of strong fresh herbs such as tarragon, oregano, thyme or crushed garlic will suffice. Add a little lemon juice and beat in a bowl or whirl in an electric blender until fluffy and smooth; then shape into a sausage and chill in the refrigerator until quite firm. The classic *maître d'hôtel* butter uses 1 tablespoon finely chopped parsley, with salt, pepper and a few drops of lemon juice.

Chopped fresh herbs such as chives, parsley, basil and dill can also be mixed into cream cheese for salads or for hors d'oeuvre dips, as well as into mayonnaise, French dressing, hollandaise or béarnaise sauce and marinades. A favourite of many cooks is the Italian sauce called *pesto* or *pistou*, based on basil, garlic, cheese and olive oil. A classic Genoese recipe for this sauce is given on page 84.

Herb jellies and jams are old favourites. To add the flavour of such fresh leaves as thyme or rosemary, follow a standard recipe for the preserve but, just before the liquid comes to a full boil, add a cupful of leaves and then continue cooking as directed in the recipe. Finally, strain the herb-preserve mixture through a jelly bag or several layers of muslin before pouring it into jam jars and sealing with porosan preserving skins. To flavour with mint, basil or parsley, brew a tea first (see directions on page 84), then strain it and use the liquid in place of part of the water called for in the standard recipe.

For a decorative touch, place a leaf of sage or scented geranium or a sprig of sweet woodruff in the bottom of each

(continued on page 84)

Herbs preserved

The ultimate fate of most herbs is to end as a memory. They become unseen ingredients in savoury stews or whiffs of fragrance from a sachet hidden in a linen drawer. But occasionally a herb product capitalizes on the charm of the living plant. One well-known herbalist flavours jellies with infusions of herbs, then tucks a sprig of the actual plant into the top of each jar as a sort of label (right). Her glittering condiments, made on a simple apple-juice base, include a golden woodruff jelly to serve with game, another golden jelly of tarragon for fish or chicken, a ruby-red rosemary jelly to accompany turkey, and a green basil jelly to glorify hamburgers. Other herbal products that perpetuate the plant material of which they are made include a splendid jar of vinegar flavoured and decorated with several herbs (overleaf) and, on pages 82-83, three arrangements made from dried herbs—a nosegay for a bride to carry, a plaited wreath to grace a festive table, and a composition of pressed herb flowers and foliage pretty enough to frame.

Brilliant as stained glass in the sun,
a pyramid of herbal jellies
decorates a herb-framed window.

A flavouring that labels itself

Vinegar, a classic preservative for foods of every kind, here preserves the very plants that give it a unique flavour. Trapped in the jar on the right are sprigs of dill, basil and burnet, a combination that adds finesse to a bowl of salad greens. Choosing herbs for such compounded vinegars is partly a matter of blending compatible flavours and partly a matter of selecting plants that complement each other visually. No less fascinating to look at but simpler to assemble are vinegars flavoured with single herbs. A sprig of mint or sage, or a cluster of chives, makes a vinegar to tempt the talents of a chef and to put proudly on kitchen display.

Burnet contributes a cucumber flavour.

Dill, much used in pickles, adds pungency and decorative punch.

Crinkly-leaved basil, redolent of summer, tastes warm and sweet.

The dill, burnet and basil aswirl in the jar on the right were picked at their prime, washed to remove dust and insects, then dried thoroughly. The vinegar is white wine vinegar, chosen for its clarity, but ordinary white malt vinegar could be used instead. To assemble the components, first tuck the herbs into the jar, then pour in the liquid, shaking lightly to remove air bubbles from the plants. Steeping time varies with the herb used from a few weeks to several months.

Unexpected delights for the eye

The beribboned nosegay of herbs below was designed for a bride to carry at her wedding—an accessory not quite as unconventional as it seems. It includes rosemary, a herb standing for devotion and fidelity that traditionally decorated the banquet halls at medieval marriages, and myrtle, which has been worn by brides in many cultures for centuries. Such an unexpected bouquet is only one example of the beauty that the artist's eye can find in these familiar plants. Other decorative uses for herbs include the autumnal wreath of dried herbs encircling the candle on the right and, lower right, pressed under glass, an attractive display of common herbs.

Lance-shaped rosemary leaves denote fidelity.

A bouquet for a bride mingles the aromatic foliage—and traditional associations—of sage, thyme, rosemary and myrtle with tiny, silvery-white pearl everlasting and dainty, pink rosebuds. Such herbal nosegays are sometimes called tussie mussies, a name whose origins are an etymological mystery.

82

Plaited together while their stems are still supple, the dried herbs in this wreath include rusty-red oregano, woolly white lamb's ears and the brown seed heads of Achillea filipendulina. The flower spikes in the foreground are artemisia, the clusters of pale brown flowers are garlic, the white flower clusters are sneezewort and the prickly pods are teasel.

Reading clockwise from the sprays of dill, top right, the herbs in this dried arrangement (below) include fan-shaped lady's mantle foliage lying on grey cotton lavender; the spear-shaped compound leaves of vitex; and lamb's ears lying on top of a sprig of thyme. Above the lamb's ears, in ascending order, are sage, burnet and rue. The scattered spiky blossoms are heather.

Artemisia bears flower spikes.

White flower clusters top ornamental chives.

A tint of purple colours sage.

Lamb's ears are woolly.

PESTO FOR PASTA

The classic Genoese sauce known as pesto is made with fresh basil leaves. Customarily spooned over pasta, this pungent green sauce is also used, a dollop at a time, to flavour soup or aubergine. To make 30 to 40 cl ($\frac{1}{2}$ to $\frac{3}{4}$ pint) of sauce combine:

60 g (2 oz) fresh basil leaves stripped from their stems, coarsely chopped
$\frac{1}{2}$ teaspoon salt
$\frac{1}{2}$ teaspoon freshly ground black pepper
1 to 2 teaspoons finely chopped garlic
2 tablespoons freshly chopped pine-nuts
25 cl (8 fl. oz) olive oil
45 g ($1\frac{1}{2}$ oz) freshly grated sardo, romano or Parmesan cheese or pecorino sardo

Crush the basil leaves and garlic together into a smooth paste in a pestle and mortar; add oil gradually.

When half the oil is used, work in the cheese and pine-nuts, the remaining oil and the seasoning. You can also make the sauce in a blender by combining the ingredients and blending them together at high speed until reduced to a thick sauce.

When your supply of fresh basil leaves runs low, try stretching it with an equal amount of fresh parsley for a basil-parsley pesto. And, for a taste of summer in midwinter, freeze pesto in small jars.

WAYS TO PERFUME THE AIR

jam jar, and pour the hot preserve over it; the leaves not only add their own taste and scent but will serve as identifying accents visible through the clear jelly. A number of herbs can be used with apple jelly; other combinations include thyme with grape or elderberry, marjoram with lemon or grapefruit, mint with gooseberry, and rosemary with orange or lemon.

Almost any of the sweet-scented herbs—rose geranium, rose petals, mint or lemon verbena—impart a delicate flavour to castor sugar used to sweeten desserts and drinks, or to icing sugar used in biscuits, icings and cakes. Put a few leaves or petals in a screw-top jar along with the sugar and it will soon take on a pleasant hint of their fragrance.

For a different kind of last-minute seasoning to sprinkle on stews, casseroles and other dishes or to use at the table, mix several finely ground dried herbs such as parsley, basil and marjoram—about a tablespoon of each, along with a little pepper or paprika—with a cup of ordinary salt; store in a shaker.

The fresh leaves of many herbs have long been used to flavour ordinary tea, hot or iced, or to make distinctive teas of their own. Among those often used to make hot herbal teas, called tisanes, are chamomile, lime flowers, sage, anise, mint, catmint, savory, marjoram, rosemary, thyme and bee balm. The last was brewed to make an American Indian beverage, known as Oswego tea, and was drunk by 18th-century colonists in protest against British taxes on Oriental tea.

Herb teas are made the same way as ordinary tea. But more leaves are required—about 2 teaspoons of freshly cut or frozen leaves or 1 teaspoon of dried leaves to one large cup. When herb teas are made with seeds or roots instead of leaves, it is necessary to make a decoction rather than an infusion—that is, the herb is added to water in a pot and boiled for 15 to 20 minutes to draw out the flavour of the fragrant oils.

Some connoisseurs of herb tea find it stimulating, while others say that it is relaxing. But all agree it is a conversation starter. Herbs are so rich in symbolism that one acquaintance of mine, an author and professional herb grower, sometimes serves what she calls Caprilands tea at her farm. It is a blend of equal parts of mint (for wisdom), rosemary (for remembrance), sage (for immortality and domestic happiness), thyme (for bravery), marjoram (for happiness), calendula (for a bright outlook and a good complexion) and chamomile (for soothed nerves and a good night's sleep).

The fragrant and decorative uses of herbs are almost as numerous as their culinary ones. Not only can attractive and sweet-smelling herbs be grown as house plants, but the leaves, flowers and even the roots of many of them can be preserved in scented potpourris, sachets and pillows.

A few decades ago almost every living room and bedroom displayed at least one jar filled with a mixture of rose petals, herb leaves and spices ready to perfume the room whenever the top was removed. Such potpourris of mingled fragrances are easy to make, and easier today than in the past.

The old-fashioned moist method, like that for preserving delicate culinary herbs, called for packing layers of partly dried leaves and petals between layers of salt in a pot; the process derived its name, from the French for pot and *pourrir*, to rot. Most people today, however, prefer the simpler method of drying the petals and leaves, which preserves the fragrances and colours just as well with much less fuss.

Almost any sweet-scented herb—orange mint, thyme, rosemary, rose geranium, lemon verbena, lemon balm, sweet marjoram, sweet basil, tarragon—can provide dried leaves for making potpourri. But the traditional starting ingredient is rose petals. To them are added flowers of lavender, lemon verbena or rose geranium, which also hold their fragrance well when dried, or almost any other garden blossom notable for its scent or colour. Snip flowers through the summer as they come into bloom, selecting only the freshest, most fragrant ones when they are at their peak; the best roses to use are old-fashioned favourites such as the apothecary rose and the damask rose, less flamboyant than modern hybrid teas but considerably more fragrant.

Pick the blossoms on a dry morning after the dew is off the petals and before the sun is high; remove the petals and place them in thin layers on drying trays like those used for leaf herbs and seeds (*page 72*). Stir the petals every day or two so that they dry evenly; if a draught threatens to blow them off the tray, cover them lightly with a piece of muslin. In four or five days they should be as dry and crackly as cornflakes. As you accumulate dried petals, keep each kind stored separately in an airtight container such as a screw-top jar, and keep the container away from light and heat.

Since the petals of some flowers retain their fragrance but lose their colour when dried, many gardeners also dry whole blossoms that will provide decorative accents in the finished jar —red bee balm, blue borage, orange calendulas and purple violets, as well as flowers of non-herbs like bachelor's buttons and delphiniums. To dry whole flowers, place them face down in

POTPOURRI INGREDIENTS

DRYING FLOWERS AND BUDS

a box or cake tin on 12 millimetres ($\frac{1}{2}$ in.) of fine sand, borax or silica gel, then add enough sand, borax or gel to cover them. Keep the blossoms in a dry, warm place for a couple of weeks until they are well dried, then carefully remove them and store them in lidded containers until you are ready to use them.

HOW TO FIX THE SCENT

To make a potpourri, empty some dried leaves and petals into a large bowl and mix them thoroughly until you get a combination of fragrances and colours that you like. To blend the scents and make them last, you will have to add a fixative; those most readily available at chemists and herbalists are ground orris root, from the root of the Florentine iris, and gum benzoin, a resin from a south-east Asian tree. Add about 2 tablespoons of crushed root or gum to each litre (1 quart) of flower petals and herb leaves.

When all the ingredients are well mixed, store them in one or more large lidded jars, keeping them less than full so you can shake or stir the mixture two or three times a week. After five or six weeks the potpourri will have cured and blended sufficiently so you can pour it into a bowl once more, give it a final stir and ladle it into decorative containers. Keep the containers covered, opening them only when you want the soft fragrance to permeate a room.

If you have a large supply of the potpourri mixture and if the ingredients are fairly bulky, you can use it to stuff small decorative pillows for a bedroom. The pillow covers should be made of a fabric porous enough to release the fragrance of the potpourri but firm enough to prevent crumbled leaves from escaping.

Smaller amounts of a potpourri mixture can be put into sachets to scent linen cupboards or dresser drawers. The mixture will repel moths if you include more pungent herbs such as tansy, wormwood, lavender, cotton lavender, rosemary and thyme or, best of all, *Artemisia camphorata*, which smells like camphor. To make a sachet, put a handful of dried leaves and petals in the centre of a handkerchief-sized piece of linen; gather the corners and tie tightly with a ribbon, leaving a loop that can be slipped over the neck of an ordinary clothes hanger. For sachets that will lie flat in a drawer or linen chest, or under a bed pillow, stitch the material into an envelope 7.5 to 15 centimetres (3 to 6 in.) square, leaving one end open; then stuff the dried mixture into the opening and stitch it closed.

FRAGRANCE FOR THE BATH

Sachets for scenting a bath can be made quite simply by tying handfuls of dried leaves or petals in squares of cheesecloth; drop one of these little bags under the hot-water tap as you start to fill the tub, then swish it around before climbing in.

For a refreshing after-bath lotion, crush a handful of fresh or dried aromatic leaves and put it into a lidded jar with bath cologne; let the jar stand for a week or so, shaking it occasionally, then strain the scented, delicately coloured liquid into small stoppered bottles for use.

Fragrant herbs such as rosemary, thyme, comfrey, basil and mint can lend a refreshing scent and colour to soap. To make a semi-soft herbal soap, prepare an extract by adding about 50 grams (2 oz) of shredded herb leaves to half a litre (16 fl. oz) of boiling water. Cover the pot, remove from the heat, then let the leaves steep for 30 minutes. Strain out and discard the leaves, and add enough water to the extract to make a third of a litre (12 fl. oz).

In the top of a double boiler, combine the herbal liquid with 80 grams (3 oz) of white bath soap cut into small pieces. Melt this mixture over boiling water until it is smooth. Then pour it into a wide-mouthed container and let it stand, uncovered, until it is cool and ready to be used.

Some gardeners make their own nosegays, old-fashioned bouquets of fresh herbs (*page 82*), to give to a bride. Others celebrate festive occasions with fragrant pomanders or spice balls—whole oranges, apples or lemons stuck solidly with cloves and trimmed with sprigs of scented herbs—or "kissing balls" made of small-mesh chicken wire stuffed with moist sphagnum moss and planted with cuttings of rosemary, cotton lavender and mistletoe. Along with a festive wassail bowl of herb-spiced punch, a decorative wreath of dried artemisia, yarrow and other herbs, and a succulent roast flavoured with thyme or sage, they are among the many joyous traditions that for centuries have rounded out the gardener's herbal year.

HOLIDAY TRADITIONS

An illustrated encyclopaedia of herbs

Whether you are looking for a particular culinary herb, an aromatic ground cover, a plant with unusual foliage or flowers, or one that will grow on a window sill as well as in the garden, the following encyclopaedia will help you to make a choice. It describes the characteristics of 127 herbs and explains in detail how to grow and use them.

Each entry indicates whether the herb is an annual, a biennial or a perennial and describes where it will grow in Europe and whether it is fully hardy. If the plant is suitable for indoor gardening, its light preferences are given, along with special soil and humidity needs.

Most herbs need abundant sunlight and a well-drained garden soil with a pH of about 6.0 to 7.5, neither very acid nor very alkaline. Otherwise they are undemanding. Generally they do not need to be fertilized. When fertilizer is used, it is commonly an organic supplement, such as well-rotted garden compost or manure, which also helps to improve drainage, or a general fertilizer. For indoor plants, a proprietary potting compost is usually recommended.

Entries also specify whether plants should be purchased from a nursery or whether they can be propagated from seed, rooted stem cuttings or root divisions. The time of year for planting and sowing is generally determined by the average date of the first or last frost. In addition, if the herb is one to be harvested, the entry gives the time and method.

The herbs are listed alphabetically according to their botanical names and are grouped by genus. For example, tarragon and its relative wormwood are included in one entry, *Artemisia*. This genus name is followed by the species names, *A. absinthium* (wormwood) and *A. dracunculus* (tarragon). Because many herbs are more commonly known by their less precise English names, these are cross-referenced in the index.

The harvest from a herb garden includes rosemary and basil, top left, and feathery dill, top right. Spriggy thyme and grey-green sage are at the bottom, and in the centre there are two fluffy flower heads of chives.

YARROW
Achillea millefolium

A

ACHILLEA
A. millefolium (yarrow, milfoil)

Yarrow is a rugged perennial, cultivated today mainly for fresh and dried flower arrangements. This pungent plant grows 60 to 90 cm (2 to 3 ft) tall, with a profusion of fern-like, grey-green leaves 5 to 7.5 cm (2 to 3 in.) long. From spring until early autumn, its tiny, white or pink blossoms form flat-topped, umbrella-shaped clusters, 5 to 7.5 cm (2 to 3 in.) in diameter.

HOW TO GROW. Yarrow is fully hardy in Europe. It needs full sun and grows rapidly in well-drained, poor to average soil. It will tolerate drought. Plants can be started from seed, but take a year or two to develop fully. More often they are propagated when root clumps are divided, as they should be every two to four years in the spring to prevent overcrowding. Plant the segments 30 to 60 cm (1 to 2 ft) apart at the same depth at which they were previously growing. To dry the flowers, cut them at their peak before they start to set seeds and hang them upside down in clusters of six to 12 in a dry, airy place out of the sun.

ACORUS
A. calamus (sweet flag, calamus)

Sweet flag is a hardy perennial aquatic or bog plant whose lemon-scented leaves and fragrant (but rather bitter-tasting) root are sometimes used for sachets. The roots were previously used in home remedies for colic. Clumps of erect, sword-shaped leaves are usually about 60 cm (2 ft) tall but can grow twice that in rich soil. The cylindrical flower spike, 5 to 10 cm (2 to 4 in.) long and studded with tiny, greenish-brown blossoms, angles out from the long stem. The creeping root, usually 2.5 to 5 cm (1 to 2 in.) thick, has brownish-red bark and a white, fleshy interior.

HOW TO GROW. Sweet flag can be grown in all parts of Europe. It flourishes in very muddy soil and full sun. It will grow in any rich garden soil that is kept moist but flowers only when growing in water. In the autumn or early spring, set root divisions 30 cm (1 ft) apart and 10 to 15 cm (4 to 6 in.) deep. Clumps of sweet flag will increase in size rapidly because of the fast-spreading roots. Leaves for drying may be picked at any time during the growing season. Roots can be harvested in early spring or late autumn after two or three years' growth, and may be dried and crumbled for sachets.

AGASTACHE
A. foeniculum, also called *A. anethiodora* (anise hyssop, fennel hyssop)

Anise hyssop is native to North America and little known in Europe. It is a handsome, 75 to 90 cm (2½ to 3 ft) tall perennial with anise-scented foliage that can be used fresh to garnish fruit cups and fresh or dried to brew aromatic tea. The coarsely toothed, oval leaves, approximately 7.5 cm (3 in.) long, are green in colour, with soft, white undersides. In midsummer, many flower spikes studded with tiny, lavender, double-lobed blossoms attract bees with their sweet-scented nectar. Each blossom has two pairs of protruding stamens, giving the plant its only resemblance to true hyssop. The botanical name is a reference to fennel (*Foeniculum vulgare*) whose foliage has a very similar scent to anise hyssop.

HOW TO GROW. Anise hyssop can be grown throughout temperate Europe, but is not recommended for hot Mediterranean regions. It adapts readily to any kind of soil. It does best in cool weather and a sunny site, though it

SWEET FLAG
Acorus calamus

ANISE HYSSOP
Agastache foeniculum

tolerates light shade. Grown from seed, the plants take two years to bloom. Sow the seeds in the autumn where the plants are to remain; they will lie dormant through the winter, germinating in the early spring.

AGRIMONIA

A. eupatoria (agrimony, cocklebur, church steeples)

Agrimony is a spiky, 60 to 90 cm (2 to 3 ft) perennial with delicately apricot-scented leaves and flowers. It is often found growing wild in grassland. The leaves are sometimes used in country wines, and one old herbal recommends it as being "good for naughty livers", but it is now used as a dye, yielding a yellow hue when gathered late in the growing season. Its green stalk is flanked by sets of compound leaves that graduate in size from 7.5 cm (3 in.) at the top to 17.5 or 20 cm (7 or 8 in.) at the bottom. The bottom sets of leaves are complex in structure, with pairs of small leaflets and pairs of saw-toothed, large leaflets alternating along the leaf stem. In summer, tiny, yellow blossoms form a spike along the top of the hairy stalk, a characteristic fancifully interpreted in the common name of church steeples. In time, these blossoms produce the hooked seed pods which inspired the name of cocklebur.

HOW TO GROW. Agrimony can be grown in northern and temperate Europe. It is easily cultivated in ordinary dry soil and will tolerate slight shade, but does better in full sun. Collect seeds from the dried stalks in the autumn and sow them 6 mm (¼ in.) deep and 17.5 cm (7 in.) apart in the spring. The plant also seeds itself readily. For quicker propagation, divide the roots early in the spring and set the segments 15 to 23 cm (6 to 9 in.) apart.

AGRIMONY
Agrimonia eupatoria

AJUGA

A. reptans (bugle, bugleweed)

Bugle is a creeping perennial that covers the ground so thickly it prevents weeds from growing and makes a popular ground cover. It is also widely—but mistakenly—planted in rock gardens, where it smothers adjacent plants. The root can be used to produce a black dye for woollens. Bugle's shiny, oval-shaped leaves, 5 to 10 cm (2 to 4 in.) long, form flat rosette clumps that spread outwards through a network of runners. Its foliage ranges in colour from deep green to various shades of reddish-purple, depending on the season of the year. In spring, brilliant blue flowers cover short spiky stems, 12.5 to 15 cm (5 to 6 in.) high. Ornamental garden cultivars are available with purple, red or white blossoms and foliage that ranges in colour from deep burgundy to green variegated with white and pink.

HOW TO GROW. Bugle grows in all parts of Europe. It flourishes under a wide range of conditions—in full sun or heavy shade and in moist or dry soil. Set young plants bought from a nursery 15 to 30 cm (6 to 12 in.) apart. The new young plants that appear at the ends of runners can easily be cut free for transplanting in the spring or autumn.

ALCHEMILLA

A. xanthochlora, also called *A. vulgaris* (lady's mantle)

A graceful, hardy perennial, 15 to 30 cm (6 to 12 in.) tall, this ground-hugging plant derives its common name from the fan-shaped, pleated leaves that were thought to resemble the folds of a medieval cloak. Tiny hairs give the leaves a silvery sheen and collect sparkling droplets of dew or rain that remain through the day; this liquid was prized by alchemists, hence the Latin name, *Alchemilla*.

BUGLE
Ajuga reptans

LADY'S MANTLE
Alchemilla xanthochlora

Today, the plant is valued for its large leaves, as much as 15 cm (6 in.) in diameter, which make a handsome ground cover. They are occasionally used fresh for soothing teas or tisanes, and in some country districts of northern England they are cooked with other herbs and flavoured leaves as a kind of purée to serve with meat. In late spring, and occasionally as late as autumn, lady's mantle bears airy clusters of small, yellow blossoms, each flower only 3 mm ($\frac{1}{8}$ in.) in diameter. The flowers are often dried for use in winter arrangements.

HOW TO GROW. This cold-loving plant grows wild in many parts of northern Europe, including Britain; it can be cultivated successfully anywhere except for the hot Mediterranean area. It tolerates shade and will grow and spread rapidly in any well-drained soil. Start seedlings in a greenhouse or cold frame in the early spring, thinning them to stand 5 cm (2 in.) apart. Move them outside when the first true leaves develop, planting them 10 to 15 cm (4 to 6 in.) apart. Lady's mantle can also be propagated by carefully dividing root clumps in the spring, setting rooted segments 10 to 15 cm (4 to 6 in.) apart to produce a thick ground cover quickly. To harvest flowers for winter bouquets, cut them at the peak of their bloom and hang them upside down to dry in a dark, airy room. Individual leaves can be dried between layers of paper for decorative use.

Lady's mantle can be grown indoors in a deep pot placed in a cool position. It should be fed with a liquid house-plant fertilizer high in nitrogen. Keep the soil damp in spring and summer, somewhat drier in winter.

ALLIUM

A. ascalonicum (shallot); *A. cepa* var. *viviparum* also called *A. cepa* var. *aggregatum* (Egyptian onion); *A. porrum* (leek); *A. sativum* (garlic); *A. schoenoprasum* (chive)

These five relatives of the onion are all perennials except for the leek, which is biennial. Three of them—shallot, Egyptian onion and garlic—are grown as annual crops for their flavoursome bulbs, though the young leaves may also be used in salads. The chive plant's hollow, grass-like leaves are chopped for seasoning, and its neat clumps and decorative lavender blossoms make it useful for borders and cut flowers. Leeks are cultivated for their blanched cylindrical stems, 15 to 25 cm (6 to 10 in.) long, which are used both as a vegetable and a seasoning.

Shallot, the most delicately flavoured of the onions, has a compound bulb divided into segments called cloves, each with its own purplish, parchment-like covering. The hollow, cylindrical, blue-green leaves form clumps about 45 cm ($1\frac{1}{2}$ ft) tall. Flowers are rare, but tiny, purple or white blossoms sometimes appear in late spring or early summer. These should be removed so as to divert the plants' energies into producing bulbs.

Garlic, like the shallot, has a compound bulb that is divided into cloves, which are enclosed in a white or purple-mottled, parchment-like covering. The sparse, flat leaves grow 45 cm ($1\frac{1}{2}$ ft) tall, and have the unmistakable garlic flavour and odour when they are crushed. In the early summer, a small, spherical cluster of white or pinkish flowers may appear at the top of a thin stalk. Treat these as shallot flowers. Garlic is used to flavour numerous savoury dishes, particularly meat, poultry and fish; it combines well with potatoes and carrots and is also popular for flavouring butters, sauces and salad dressings.

Chives, the smallest of the onions, appear each growing season in lush, grass-like clumps 20 to 30 cm (8 to 12 in.) high. The fluffy balls of flowers, 2 to 2.5 cm ($\frac{3}{4}$ to 1 in.) in diameter, bloom on slender stems in the early summer; although decorative, these should be removed as soon as

SHALLOT
Allium ascalonicum

EGYPTIAN ONION
Allium cepa var. *viviparum*

possible otherwise the plants cease to produce tender young leaves for seasoning. The finely chopped or snipped leaves are used fresh as seasoning and to garnish cold soups, egg dishes, salads and dressings and with buttered fresh vegetables. They are also used in tartare sauce and in *fines herbes* mixtures.

Egyptian onion is an odd-looking onion, forming a crown of small brown bulbils at the top of a 60 to 90 cm (2 to 3 ft) tubular stem called a scape. As the weight of this bulbous head increases, the entire scape dips to the ground and the bulbils take root to produce new plants. The Egyptian onion's hollow, dark blue-green leaves, swollen at the base, reach only half way up the scape; the underground bulb develops hardly at all. The bulbils give a delicate flavour to cooked dishes or salads and are sometimes pickled as cocktail onions.

The leek is grown as an annual vegetable, but, if a few plants are left in the ground for a second season, they develop stalks from which emerge globe-shaped flower heads, 7.5 to 10 cm (3 to 4 in.) across, consisting of numerous tiny, purple blossoms. The white underground part of the leek is cooked as a vegetable, but the green upper parts of young leeks can also be used, freshly chopped, to flavour soups and stocks.

HOW TO GROW. All five plants thrive throughout Europe, though garlic needs a longer and warmer growing season than is normally found in northern Europe. They grow best in full sun and rich soil, and should be planted outdoors in the early spring.

Shallots do well in soil with a pH of 5.5 to 7.0. Plants started from seed require two years to mature, and most shallots are consequently grown from cloves; planted in the autumn in frost-free regions, they mature in about nine months. Usually shallots are planted in February and will mature by July and August. Plant the cloves 15 cm (6 in.) apart, setting them deep enough to let the tips just show above ground level. When the leaves are 12.5 to 15 cm (5 to 6 in.) tall, apply 5:10:5 fertilizer at the rate of 85 grams (3 oz) per 3 metres (10 ft) of row. By midsummer, the shallots will have formed clusters of three to 10 cloves. When the foliage becomes partially withered, dig the cloves up and dry them by placing them in a dry, shady spot for two to three weeks before storing.

Garlic is grown in a similar way, in soil with a pH of 5.5 to 8.0. Break a garlic bulb into single cloves and place each clove 5 cm (2 in.) deep and 10 to 15 cm (4 to 6 in.) apart. Fertilize in the same way as shallots. In midsummer, when the leaves turn yellow, dig up the plants and store as for shallots. To speed ripening, bend down the tops as they begin to turn yellow to limit growth.

Chives grow best in soil with a pH of 6.0 to 7.0. Propagated from seed, they take about a year to produce harvest-ready leaves. Sow the seeds in rows in the spring, covering them with 6 to 12 mm ($\frac{1}{4}$ to $\frac{1}{2}$ in.) of soil. Do not thin the plants the first year. Early the following spring, transplant small clusters of seedlings 15 cm (6 in.) apart, leaving six or more bulbs in each cluster. Chives planted as rooted clumps—the more common procedure—are set about 5 cm (2 in.) deep and 30 cm (1 ft) apart. Though chives are usually planted in the spring, in very warm regions where the summer temperature remains over 32°C (90°F) for prolonged periods they can be planted in the autumn for a winter harvest. Chives spread rapidly in rich, moist soil. Should the plants weaken from repeated cutting, hoe a light dusting of 5:10:5 fertilizer into the soil. Renew the plants every two to four years by dividing the roots and replanting them in soil that has been enriched with an abundance of organic matter.

Egyptian onion grows best in soil with a pH of 6.0 to

LEEK
Allium porrum

GARLIC
Allium sativum

CHIVE
Allium schoenoprasum

ALOE
Aloe barbadensis

MARSH MALLOW
Althaea officinalis

7.0. Set the bulbils in rows 10 to 20 cm (4 to 8 in.) apart and 12 mm (½ in.) deep, in late summer, autumn or spring. During the summer, treat in the same way as shallots. When new bulbils appear in late summer, cut off the entire top growth; fresh leaves will appear to permit a continuing harvest of greens. The cut stalks, with their clusters of bulbils, may be tied in bunches and hung in a cool, dry place for use during the winter.

Leeks do best in a moist, fertile soil with a pH of 6.0 to 8.0. For a maincrop, sow leeks in a prepared seed bed outdoors in mid-spring. In early summer, when the seedlings have reached a height of 10 to 12.5 cm (4 to 5 in.), prepare a trench 30 cm (1 ft) deep and 15 cm (6 in.) wide and fill in the bottom 15 cm (6 in.) with a layer of compost. Trim the tops and roots of the seedlings and drop them into 15 cm (6 in.) deep holes, 15 to 20 cm (6 to 8 in.) apart. Do not firm in the seedlings, but water them in well so that only the tips show above the soil. If more than one row is required, allow 38 to 45 cm (1¼ to 1½ ft) between the trenches. As the plants mature, fill the trench gradually to shield the base of the plants from light and blanch them. Every three to four weeks scatter 140 grams (5 oz) of 5:10:5 fertilizer per 3 metres (10 ft) of row along each side. Leeks mature in about four and a half months but are edible at any stage; when they are young, they are sometimes used raw as a substitute for salad onions.

Chives, Egyptian onion and garlic can be grown successfully indoors on sunny window sills, although the bulbils of Egyptian onion and the bulbs of garlic will not develop to any extent. Pot clumps of chives in the autumn, then leave them outside in cool temperatures for about a month before you move them indoors to provide fresh leaves throughout the winter. Plant Egyptian onions and garlic indoors at any time using a proprietary potting compost. In seven to 10 days shoots will be visible; when they are 7.5 cm (3 in.) tall, the leaves can be cut for use.

ALOE
A. barbadensis, also called *A. vera* and *A. vulgaris* (aloe, true aloe, bitter aloe, Barbados aloe)

Aloe is a succulent perennial whose fleshy leaves contain a bitter, yellow juice used in cosmetics and ointments for insect bites and sunburn. The sap is used in the manufacture of bitters, such as the French Fernet Branca, and in medication to discourage nail-biting in children. Most gardeners, however, grow the herb as an interesting addition to their indoor plants. The thick, leathery, strap-like green leaves grow to a length of 15 to 60 cm (6 to 24 in.). They are usually edged with soft spines and, when young, are dotted with white spots. Old plants send up leafless blossom stalks that rise from the centre of the leaf rosettes to bear plumes of yellow or reddish, bell-like flowers; however, pot-grown aloes rarely bloom.

HOW TO GROW. A semi-desert plant, true aloe can be grown outdoors only in hot Mediterranean climates. However, aloe grows easily anywhere in pots as a house plant or summer terrace plant. If kept on a terrace, the plant must be moved inside when the temperature drops below 10°C (50°F). Aloe does best if it has four or more hours a day of direct sunlight, but it will grow fairly well in bright, indirect light.

Potted aloes need very little care: they thrive for years without repotting. Allow the soil to become fairly dry between thorough waterings. In winter, too much water is hazardous; let the soil become quite dry between waterings.

Do not fertilize the first year after potting. Subsequently, feed once a year, in the autumn, with liquid house-plant fertilizer diluted to half the recommended strength; this increases the chance of flowering. The simplest way to propagate aloe is to detach the small rooted suckers that develop around its base, and then plant them in pots of sandy soil.

ALOYSIA See *Lippia*

ALTHAEA
A. officinalis (marsh mallow)

Marsh mallow, a flowering perennial, takes its common name from the coastal marshes that are its natural habitat in Europe. Its tender leaves and tops were formerly eaten as a raw salad or cooked vegetable and the starchy and sweet roots were used by countryfolk to produce a sweetmeat, marshmallow. This name has persisted, though marshmallow today is made from gelatine, commercial starch and sugar, and the plant is now mainly grown for its decorative qualities. A relative of the hollyhock, marsh mallow has erect stems, 0.9 to 1.2 metres (3 to 4 ft) high, and pale pink to rose-coloured flowers, 2.5 to 4 cm (1 to 1½ in.) across. The flowers spring singly or in clusters from the axils of the upper leaves, and bloom in late summer. Marsh mallow's maple-like leaves are a velvety, soft grey-green and have serrated edges.

HOW TO GROW. Marsh mallow grows throughout Europe, though it does not flourish in the hot, dry summers of southern Europe. It does best in bright sun and a light, sandy, moist soil. Sow seeds indoors in the spring in seed trays, or outdoors in summer as soon as ripe seeds are available. When seedlings are 5 to 7.5 cm (2 to 3 in.) high, thin or transplant them, spacing them 30 to 45 cm (1 to 1½ ft) apart. For quicker results grow marsh mallow from root divisions in the spring. Use a sharp knife to divide the fleshy root to include a bud in each piece.

AMARACUS See *Origanum*

ANCHUSA
A. officinalis (alkanet, bugloss)

Alkanet is a biennial bearing cucumber-tasting flowers that can be floated in wine punches and fruit cups for flavouring and garnish; the root bark provides a red dye. From midsummer until the early autumn, the 30 to 60 cm (1 to 2 ft) high plant produces clusters of tiny blue, violet or purple blossoms. The hairy, lance-like leaves, 7.5 to 15 cm (3 to 6 in.) long and 2.5 cm (1 in.) wide, are dark green and have a rough texture.

HOW TO GROW. Alkanet is fully hardy and does best in the relatively cool summers of northern and temperate Europe. It thrives in full sun but tolerates partial shade. Provide good, well-drained soil supplemented with well-rotted garden compost or manure. Plants can be started in the spring from seeds or root divisions, and in the autumn from root cuttings. When started from seed, plants take a year to reach maturity. Sow the seeds about 6 mm (¼ in.) deep; when the seedlings are 2.5 to 5 cm (1 to 2 in.) high, transplant them about 30 cm (1 ft) apart. Cutting back the faded flowers encourages additional blossoming. In late autumn, mulch the plants lightly—in damp climates, the pulpy roots are prone to rot under a deep mulch.

To start plants from root cuttings, place 5 cm (2 in.) lengths upright in pots of a proprietary potting compost, covering the tips about 2.5 cm (1 in.) deep. Place the pots in a cold frame for the duration of the winter and set the new plants outdoors in the garden in the spring.

ALKANET
Anchusa officinalis

DILL
Anethum graveolens

ANGELICA
Angelica archangelica

ANETHUM

A. graveolens, also called *Peucedanum graveolens* (dill)

Dill is a hardy annual with slightly sweet, anise-tasting leaves that are used to flavour soups, vegetables, salads, sauces and fish, and with pungent, somewhat bitter seeds that are used as an ingredient in pickles and in sauerkraut dishes. The thread-like, blue-green leaves spread out in feathery branches from a hollow stalk 60 to 90 cm (2 to 3 ft) high. From June to October, if successive sowings are made, the plant produces umbrella clusters of tiny, yellow flowers that ripen into small, thin, brown seeds.

HOW TO GROW. Dill grows outdoors in all parts of Europe and can also be cultivated indoors as a pot plant. In the garden, it requires full sun and an acid soil—pH 5.5 to 6.5—supplemented with well-rotted garden compost or manure. Select a protected site, since the hollow stalks, top-heavy with blossoms, can be easily knocked over by the wind. For summer and autumn crops, sow seeds about twice a month from early spring to midsummer, setting them 6 mm ($\frac{1}{4}$ in.) deep in rows 60 cm (2 ft) apart. For an early spring crop, sow seeds in the autumn before the ground freezes. In frost-free areas, sow seeds from late summer through to midwinter for crops to mature in winter and spring. Thin the seedlings when they are about 5 cm (2 in.) high so that the plants stand about 25 to 30 cm (10 to 12 in.) apart. (Transplanting is difficult because the root structure is so delicate.) If the plants appear weak when they reach 30 cm (1 ft) tall, hoe in a general fertilizer at the rate of 85 grams (3 oz) to a 3 metre (10 ft) row. In most regions, the plants will be killed by the first frost, but self-sown seeds often germinate to provide successive years' crops. Do not grow dill near fennel because this relative may cross-pollinate and the flavour of the resulting seeds and leaves is impossible to predict.

Dill grown indoors needs at least five hours a day of direct sunlight or 12 hours of bright artificial light. Fill 15 cm (6 in.) pots with potting compost moistened with lukewarm water. Scatter about six seeds over the surface. Wrap the pot in a clear plastic bag to keep the soil moist, and set it in a brightly lit but not sunny place where the temperature is 18° to 24°C (65° to 75°F). When true leaves appear, remove the plastic bag and place the pot in a sunny window. Keep the soil moist but not wet. When the plants reach a height of 7.5 to 10 cm (3 to 4 in.), thin them to the three strongest plants in each pot. For a continuous supply of dill, two or three pots should be ample if you take cuttings from each pot in turn.

From indoor or outdoor plants, dill leaves can be cut at any time and can be used fresh, dried or frozen, although dried leaves lose much of their flavour and frozen ones are unsuitable for garnishing. Fresh dill leaves should be finely chopped for flavouring. The seeds can be used fresh or dried. Separate the seeds from the flower heads by placing the cut stalks in a paper bag and shaking them; spread the seeds on a flat surface to dry, then store them in an airtight container.

ANGELICA

A. archangelica (angelica)

Angelica is a giant relative of parsley that grows 1.2 to 2 metres (4 to 7 ft) high. It is a biennial or short-lived perennial, usually grown from summer-sown seed, but its life can be extended if the plant is prevented from flowering and bearing fruit. Every part of angelica is useful. Its somewhat bitter-tasting leaves are boiled and eaten like spinach or dried for medicinal teas; finely chopped they also impart a musky flavour to rhubarb dishes. The young, hollow stems can be boiled like rhubarb but are most often candied and used as a decoration on pastries, cakes, sweets and desserts. The juniper-flavoured seeds can be substituted for real juniper berries in flavouring gin; oil from the roots flavours various liqueurs; and dried roots are ground for sachets.

In the first year angelica produces leaves but no stalk and it seldom grows more than 60 to 90 cm (2 to 3 ft) high. In the second year, or sometimes the third, the plant shoots up a flower stalk to its full dramatic height and is capped in early summer with clusters or umbels of greenish-white flowers which are followed by 12 mm ($\frac{1}{2}$ in.), straw-textured yellow fruit, each containing a single 6 mm ($\frac{1}{4}$ in.), brown seed. If the stalk is cut before flowers form, the plant lives another year; if the flowers are allowed to go to seed, the plant dies, but seedlings will appear in the garden.

HOW TO GROW. Angelica is native to Europe and thrives in all regions. It does best in moist, slightly acid loam with a pH of 6.5 to 7.0. Plant it in a cool, partially shaded site. It is ordinarily raised from seed, but sow the seeds 6 mm ($\frac{1}{4}$ in.) deep immediately after they ripen, because they quickly lose their germinating ability. If they have to be saved until the following spring, store them in a refrigerator. Sow a pinch of seeds where you want them to grow, at 75 to 90 cm ($2\frac{1}{2}$ to 3 ft) intervals. When they germinate about three weeks later, thin to leave only the strongest plant at each site. Angelica seedlings can be transplanted but not mature plants. If the stalks are cut back in the second year, the roots will send up new shoots that can be transplanted. Roots intended for use as flavouring should be dug up during the autumn of the first year, when they are at their most tender. The leaves and stalks should be harvested during the second year; the stems are best during the spring before the flowers begin to open.

ANISUM See *Pimpinella*

ANTHEMIS
A. nobilis (chamomile, Roman chamomile)

This aromatic, low-growing perennial makes a soft, lush ground cover much used in Europe as a grass substitute for lawns. It can be mowed and is drought resistant. The whole plant has a pleasantly pungent fragrance. The stems lie flat and creep along the ground, rooting as they go, creating a feathery, grey-green mat 7.5 to 25 cm (3 to 10 in.) high, depending upon the fertility of the soil. During midsummer, flower stems rise 30 to 35 cm (12 to 14 in.) high and bear 2 cm ($\frac{3}{4}$ in.) white, daisy-like blossoms; the cultivar 'Treneague' is recommended for lawns because it does not produce flowers.

The dried flower heads are still popular in hot tisanes for the relief of head colds, and the oil extracted from the flowers has some cosmetic uses in soaps and body and hair lotions. It is also used to flavour some aperitifs, but it does not enter into the manufacture of the Manzanilla sherry which is named after a place, not after the similar Spanish name for chamomile.

HOW TO GROW. Chamomile grows throughout Europe in almost any well-drained soil. Though it will tolerate some shade, it does best in full sun. Plants are most easily propagated from root divisions taken in the autumn or early spring. To grow from seed, sow indoors in midwinter on a sunny window sill and transplant to individual pots when the first true leaves appear. Set the new plants outdoors in the spring, as close as 10 cm (4 in.) apart for ground cover, 20 to 25 cm (8 to 10 in.) apart for row planting. Keep the soil moist but not soggy until the plants are well established.

CHAMOMILE
Anthemis nobilis

CHERVIL
Anthriscus cerefolium

HORSERADISH
Armoracia rusticana

ANTHRISCUS
A. cerefolium (chervil)

Chervil, one of the classic *fines herbes* of French cooking, is an annual grown for its anise or parsley-flavoured leaves, which intensify the flavours of other herbs. It is a member of the parsley family and its lacy leaves somewhat resemble those of parsley but are a lighter green and more feathery. Within eight weeks after sowing, chervil produces umbrella-shaped clusters of small, white blossoms on 45 to 60 cm (1½ to 2 ft) long, hollow stems. The flowers ripen into slender black seeds. By cutting back the flower heads before they bloom, you can stimulate new leaf growth. Chervil loses its delicate flavour quickly when cooked and should only be added, finely chopped, to soups and sauces at the last minute. The fresh leaves also add a piquant flavour to salads, fresh vegetables and salad dressings; they do not dry or freeze well, but in many European countries tinned chervil is widely available.

HOW TO GROW. Chervil can be grown outdoors in all parts of Europe though less successfully in hot Mediterranean climates and can be grown indoors as a pot plant. It grows best in partial shade and a light, moist garden soil, pH 6.0 to 7.0, supplemented with well-rotted garden compost or manure. It is harmed by hot weather and high humidity, and it does not easily survive transplanting. Seeds can be sown at any time of the year, but they germinate best in cool weather; sow them at intervals of three to four weeks from early spring until late autumn. In warm climates, sow seeds in late summer and autumn for winter and spring harvests. Press the seeds lightly into the soil, and when the seedlings are 7.5 to 10 cm (3 to 4 in.) high, thin them to stand 15 to 23 cm (6 to 9 in.) apart. Plants that are left to flower will reseed themselves, and a few plants can be permitted to bloom for this purpose.

Chervil grown indoors in pots does best with four or five hours a day of direct sunlight or 12 hours of strong artificial light. It thrives in cool temperatures, under 15°C (60°F). Fill 15 cm (6 in.) pots with a proprietary potting compost, moistened with lukewarm water. Sprinkle a few seeds on the surface. Slip each pot into a clear plastic bag and place in a sunny window. Keep the soil moist. Remove the plastic bags when the seedlings appear and, when they are 2.5 to 5 cm (1 to 2 in.) high, thin to three in each pot.

Fresh harvests can be made from chervil plants at one-month intervals if the top leaves only are removed each time. Such pinching back will encourage new growth.

ARMORACIA
A. rusticana, also called *Cochlearia armoracia* (horseradish)

Horseradish is a hardy perennial cultivated for its sharp-tasting white root, which is grated or pounded for a table condiment and is the traditional accompaniment to roast beef. The plant's coarse, wavy leaves spread outwards in a radius of 60 to 90 cm (2 to 3 ft), and in summer a slender stalk bearing small, faintly scented, white flowers rises to a height of 90 cm (3 ft). The tiny fruit pods usually fail to mature, so horseradish is always propagated from root cuttings called thongs. Thick, white and long-lived, the taproot reaches deep into the soil, and its numerous branching side roots and suckers make the plant difficult to remove from the garden once it is established. Three plants will yield enough horseradish for an average family.

HOW TO GROW. Horseradish, hardy throughout Europe, will grow in any moist garden soil that is supplemented with manure or well-rotted garden compost but kept relatively neutral with a pH of about 7.0. Plant 15 to 20 cm (6 to 8 in.) long root cuttings in early spring, spacing the segments 60 cm (2 ft) apart and setting them in the ground at a slant or vertically, thick ends up, so that the top of each cutting is 7.5 to 10 cm (3 to 4 in.) below ground level. Firm the soil well after planting. Since horseradish is a rampant grower, the roots should be confined to one bed. In early summer, dig round each plant and carefully rub off the side roots to ensure a well-formed taproot. Do not dig the plants up to remove these side roots; horseradish is delicate and can easily be damaged if it is handled roughly.

To harvest for storing, dig up a root in the early autumn, when it is at its tastiest, and store in cool, moist sand until needed. Alternatively, the roots can be peeled and grated immediately and preserved in distilled or white wine vinegar. The latter method, however, results in a substantial loss of flavour.

ARTEMISIA
A. absinthium (wormwood); *A. dracunculus* (tarragon, French tarragon, estragon)

Though of the same genus, these two artemisias differ greatly in personality. Wormwood is one of the "bitter herbs" of the Bible; it is used in the flavouring of several aperitifs, notably vermouth and absinthe, the popular French drink which, when taken in excess, can have disastrous effects. As a concentrate, wormwood is a narcotic drug, with alarming side-effects. Tarragon is one of the great and classic herbs of European cooking, essential in *fines herbes* mixtures and béarnaise sauce; the subtle anise flavour of its leaves complements veal, chicken, fish, eggs, salad dressings and mayonnaise and provides the distinctive ingredient in tarragon vinegar.

Both plants are perennials with tough, slender stems that may become somewhat woody and have a habit of sprawling late in the summer. Wormwood grown in gardens as an ornament becomes 60 to 120 cm (2 to 4 ft) high and has deeply cut, silvery-grey leaves. Both leaves and stems are covered with downy hairs, giving the plant a delicate, chalky appearance that contrasts with the greens of other plants in the garden. In midsummer, small, greenish-yellow blossoms appear. Both the leaves and flowers have a pungent odour.

Tarragon grows 60 to 90 cm (2 to 3 ft) tall and its leaves are long, narrow and dark green. In midsummer tiny, greenish-white flowers bloom but they do not set seeds in moderate or cooler climates; consequently tarragon is mainly grown from cuttings or root division. Where the plants thrive they quickly spread by underground runners.

HOW TO GROW. Wormwood, hardy throughout Europe, thrives in sun or partial shade and in almost any soil. It can be raised from seed, which germinates best when sown in the autumn, but it is usually started in the early spring from root divisions. It can also be propagated from stem cuttings taken in early summer. Set seedlings, rooted stem cuttings or root divisions 45 to 60 cm (1½ to 2 ft) apart, to allow for the plant's spreading habit. Tall stems can be staked or trimmed back. In areas with heavy frost, cut the plants to the ground in autumn and cover them with a light mulch of straw after the ground has frozen.

Tarragon is hardy in temperate and southern Europe; it cannot survive winters in northern Europe and is difficult to grow in hot, dry Mediterranean climates. It does best in full sun and a well-drained, slightly sandy soil with a pH of 6.0 to 7.5. Buy plants from reliable sources because sometimes the inferior and more bitter Russian tarragon is sold as "French tarragon". Tarragon seeds sold commercially are also usually Russian tarragon. Set plants in the ground in the early spring, 45 to 60 cm (1½ to 2 ft) apart. In early summer, after cutting the first crop of leaves, hoe a

WORMWOOD
Artemisia absinthium

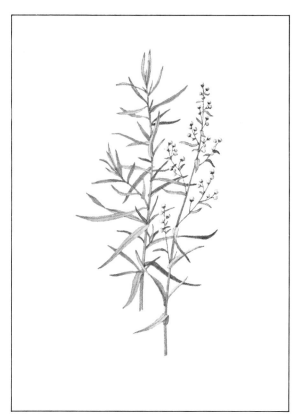
TARRAGON
Artemisia dracunculus

SEA PURSLANE
Atriplex hortensis

BORAGE
Borago officinalis

handful of fertilizer into the soil around the base of each plant. Tarragon is apt to die over the winter if prolonged frosts or heavy rainfalls occur, but often grows up again from the base in spring; the best precaution is a well-drained site and plenty of space between plants. In northern areas it should be mulched in winter with bracken or straw. Every three or four years, dig up the tarragon in the spring, when the plant is 5 to 7.5 cm (2 to 3 in.) high, and divide the roots of each plant into several smaller clumps for transplanting.

Tarragon can be cut for flavouring at any time. To dry or freeze leaves for winter use, cut the stems 7.5 cm (3 in.) from the ground in early summer and again in early autumn. Lay them flat or hang them in loose bunches in a dark, airy place; when dry, crumble the leaves and store in an airtight container.

Tarragon grown indoors needs at least five hours of direct sunlight a day. Use a proprietary potting compost. Pot tarragon for indoor use no later than midsummer; most tarragon potted later dies even if temperatures are warm and light conditions are excellent.

ASPERULA See *Galium*

ATRIPLEX
A. hortensis (sea purslane, orach, French spinach)

Sea purslane is a tall, erect annual that shoots up to a height of 1.5 to 1.8 metres (5 to 6 ft) in a single season. The arrowhead-shaped leaves, up to 12.5 cm (5 in.) long and sprinkled with a crystalline substance, are sometimes eaten as a spinach substitute or used in salads. However, it is chiefly grown at the back of an annual border for its ornamental foliage. The cultivar 'Rubra' has deep red leaves, an effective contrast with green foliage both in the garden and in flower arrangements. In summer, sea purslane bears inconspicuous flowers on short stalks that grow along the main stem.

HOW TO GROW. Sea purslane needs full sun and grows in any light, well-drained soil. The plant survives in dry soil, but the leaves are most edible if the soil is kept moist enough to produce succulent growth. Sow the seeds 6 to 12 mm ($\frac{1}{4}$ to $\frac{1}{2}$ in.) deep as early in the spring as the ground can be worked. Thin the seedlings so that the plants stand 20 to 30 cm (8 to 12 in.) apart. If seeds are to be saved, gather them just before the pods open so that they do not blow away. The plant seeds itself readily, and therefore some gardeners consider it to be a weed.

B

BORAGO
B. officinalis (borage, bee bread, star flower)

An annual reaching 30 to 60 cm (1 to 2 ft) tall, borage has cucumber-tasting leaves used to flavour salads, cream-cheese spreads and summer drinks; its sky blue, white or occasionally pink flowers are floated on chilled wine cups or candied for cake decorations. Both the leaves and stems of borage are covered with fine hairs that become woolly and rough as the plant ages; therefore only fresh young leaves and stems, finely chopped, are used for flavouring. The star-shaped flowers, which bloom from spring to midsummer, attract bees, hence the name bee bread. Because the flowers are pendulous, borage is often planted on a steep slope so the drooping heads are clearly visible from below.

HOW TO GROW. Borage, native to Europe, requires full sun and does best in infertile, relatively light, dry soil with a pH of 6.0 to 7.0. Sow the seeds in the garden, where they are to grow, in the autumn or very early spring, 3 to 6 mm ($\frac{1}{8}$ to $\frac{1}{4}$ in.) deep, because borage is difficult to transplant successfully except when very small. When the seedlings are 5 to 7.5 cm (2 to 3 in.) high, thin them to stand 25 to 30 cm (10 to 12 in.) apart. Keep the soil moist while the plants are young. Borage seeds will keep for up to eight years. Plants seed themselves readily, coming up year after year without attention.

BRASSICA See *Sinapis*

BUXUS
B. sempervirens (common box)
Although not itself a herb, the low-growing, evergreen box is included in this encyclopaedia because it was a favourite hedge plant in Elizabethan knot gardens, where it was used to separate the various herb plots from each other. It has the additional advantage of lending itself happily to severe clipping and is an ideal subject for artistic forms of topiary. Left to grow unhindered, box may eventually reach a height of 3 metres (10 ft) and a spread of half that, but it is extremely slow growing; the dwarf cultivar 'Suffruticosa' is one of the best forms for low hedges. The oval leaves are glistening green and set on either side of the square branches. In late spring, box bears tiny, greenish flowers with a delicious honey perfume.

HOW TO GROW. Box is hardy throughout Europe and will grow in any kind of soil, in full sun or light shade. Hedges are best planted in early autumn or, failing that, in spring. Set the young plants 30 cm (1 ft) apart and cut them back by at least a third after planting to encourage bushy and branching growth from low down. Once the hedge is established it needs to be pruned to shape only once a year, usually in late summer. Box is increased from stem cuttings in late summer; root them in peat and sand in a cold frame and transplant them to a nursery bed the next spring for growing on for another couple of years before setting them out in their permanent positions.

C
CALENDULA
C. officinalis (calendula, pot marigold)
Few plants are easier to grow than the calendula, an annual that is one of the most decorative of all herbs. It reaches 30 to 45 cm (1 to $1\frac{1}{2}$ ft) in height and produces orange or yellow flowers; the petals are used for food colouring and as an inexpensive substitute for saffron. The furry stems are clasped by pale green leaves that may be 15 cm (6 in.) long. All summer the brilliant flowers, 5 to 10 cm (2 to 4 in.) across, open in the early morning and close at dusk. They are striking in a flower bed and in flower arrangements.

HOW TO GROW. Calendulas grow in most parts of Europe, in almost any soil, although they do best in rich, loamy soil; they need full sun. In frost-free regions, a late summer or early autumn sowing will provide winter and spring flowers. When seedlings are 10 to 15 cm (4 to 6 in.) high, thin or transplant them to stand 25 to 30 cm (10 to 12 in.) apart. Calendula plants blossom continuously from early summer until the autumn. To encourage continuous flowering, nip off the faded blossoms before they set seed.

To harvest calendula petals, strip them from the newly opened flowers and use them fresh or dried. To dry them,

COMMON BOX
Buxus sempervirens

Illustration by Pamela Freeman

CALENDULA
Calendula officinalis

MARSH MARIGOLD
Caltha palustris

LADY'S SMOCK
Cardamine pratensis

lay them on paper in a cool, dark, airy room so that they do not touch one another, and turn them frequently. When the petals are crisp, store them in an airtight container.

To grow calendulas indoors, sow seeds outdoors in midsummer and transplant seedlings to 15 cm (6 in.) pots filled with a proprietary potting compost. Bring plants indoors to a sunny window sill before severe frost. They do best with night temperatures of 10°C (50°F), daytime readings of 15° to 18°C (60° to 65°F). Keep the soil barely moist; if it is allowed to become soggy, the roots may rot. Plants require at least five hours of direct sunlight or 12 hours of strong artificial light.

CALTHA
C. palustris (marsh marigold, kingcup)

Marsh marigold is a hardy perennial commonly found in wet and marshy places. It resembles a giant buttercup with its glistening, golden-yellow flowers dusted with golden pollen. The flowers, 2.5 cm (1 in.) or more across, open in late spring and early summer and are borne above the glossy, deep green, kidney-shaped leaves. Today, marsh marigold is grown as an ornamental plant, but it was formerly also grown for culinary purposes: the chopped leaves were added to meat stews, and the young, unopened flower buds were pickled like nasturtium seeds as a substitute for capers. For garden decoration, the double-flowered cultivar 'Plena' is the one most frequently cultivated; it grows about 25 cm (10 in.) high, with many-branched stems topped by double blooms of rich golden petals and light green centres.

HOW TO GROW. Marsh marigolds are hardy throughout Europe. The wild marsh marigold flourishes near water, but the cultivated forms will grow in any ordinary garden soil provided this is kept moist and cool. It thrives in rich loam, preferably slightly acid, in sun or light shade. The easiest method of propagation is by division of the fleshy roots in early summer after flowering is finished. The roots come apart easily, but must be set in moist ground immediately to prevent shrivelling.

CARDAMINE
C. pratensis (lady's smock, cuckoo flower, bitter-cress)

Lady's smock, which flowers around the time the first cuckoo is heard, is a pretty little perennial commonly seen in moist meadows and other grassy places. It is related to watercress, and the leaves can be used as a salad ingredient or as a garnish. Lady's smock grows 25 to 30 cm (10 to 12 in.) high, with thin, delicate stems set with green pinnate leaves which sometimes root where they touch the ground. The flowers are set in a cross pattern of four petals; they are pale lilac in colour and borne on the stems in loose sprays.

HOW TO GROW. Lady's smock grows wild throughout temperate and northern Europe, preferably in moist, acid soil, in sun or light shade. New plants can be raised from seeds gathered in early summer and sown outdoors as soon as they are ripe; they usually take two years to reach flowering size. Roots can be divided in early spring. Where the leaves have rooted and formed small new plants, these can be dug up and set out in the garden, being spaced about 25 cm (10 in.) apart.

CARTHAMUS
C. tinctorius (safflower, saffron thistle, false saffron)

An annual, 60 to 90 cm (2 to 3 ft) tall, safflower bears colourful flowers from which carthamin dye is obtained and used for colouring foods, textiles and cosmetics (it is a principal ingredient of rouge). Safflower is grown as a commercial crop in India, and oil extracted from its seeds is a popular salad oil, since it is low in cholesterol. The dried seed heads are also useful in winter flower arrangements.

The dark green leaves are spiny; the 2.5 cm (1 in.), ball-like flowers, which bloom in midsummer, have deep yellow florets that deepen into orange as the season progresses. The flowers are followed by tooth-like, white seeds, the source of the oil, which ripen by the end of summer.

HOW TO GROW. Safflower does best in warm southern regions with scarce summer rainfalls, but will also grow in more temperate climates. Excessive rain tends to spread disease among its leaves and to cause newly ripened seeds to germinate while still on the stalk. It needs full sun, thrives in poor, light, dry soil and reseeds itself. Sow seeds 6 mm ($\frac{1}{4}$ in.) deep in the spring, when all danger of frost has passed. Sow them where the plants are to remain, since safflower is hard to transplant. Seedlings should be thinned to stand 10 to 15 cm (4 to 6 in.) apart.

Until the prickly spines develop, the tender leaves and stems are appealing to rabbits, so it is a good idea to protect the young plants with fine-mesh screens. Cut and dry the flower heads in late summer to make the saffron-like powder for use in cooking; store the dried petals in an airtight container and grind or pound them as they are needed.

CARUM
C. carvi (caraway)

Caraway is most often grown for its seeds, which contribute a liquorice-like flavour to many German and Austrian recipes for cakes, biscuits, cheese, breads and liqueurs. The seeds are also sprinkled over vegetables and salads. But the feathery leaves, resembling carrot tops, can be used when young as a salad ingredient, and in some east-European countries the long, pale yellow taproots are also cooked and eaten as vegetables. A hardy biennial, caraway produces only a 15 to 20 cm (6 to 8 in.) mound of leaves the first year; the following spring, a thin flower stalk shoots up 60 to 90 cm (2 to 3 ft), bearing flat clusters of tiny, off-white flowers that ripen into 6 mm ($\frac{1}{4}$ in.), brown, crescent-shaped seeds. When the seeds mature, the plant dies. Caraway often seeds itself if the seed heads are not harvested before they break open.

HOW TO GROW. Caraway grows wild throughout Europe and is fully hardy. It will grow in almost any well-drained soil with a pH of 6.0 to 7.0, but it needs full sun. Sow seeds in the autumn or early spring, setting them 3 mm ($\frac{1}{8}$ in.) deep in rows 60 cm (2 ft) apart. Germination is slow except when seeds are sown fresh, immediately after harvesting. When seedlings reach a height of 5 cm (2 in.), thin plants to stand 15 to 30 cm (6 to 12 in.) apart. Caraway plants do best if they are not transplanted.

To harvest caraway seeds, cut seed heads off in late summer as soon as the seeds turn brown; if they are left on the plant until thoroughly dry, they will scatter. Seeds to be used in cooking should be scalded immediately after picking to kill any insects that may be in them. Scald the freshly picked seeds in boiling water; then dry them in the sun for several days, bringing them inside at night. When dry, store them in an airtight jar. Seeds intended for future sowing should not be scalded because the heat kills the seed embryos.

CHAMOMILLA See *Matricaria*

SAFFLOWER
Carthamus tinctorius

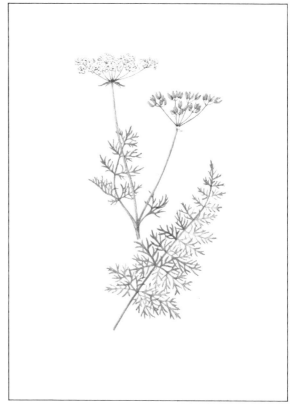

CARAWAY
Carum carvi

GOOD KING HENRY
Chenopodium bonus-henricus

CHENOPODIUM
C. album (fat hen); *C. bonus-henricus* (Good King Henry)

These two weed-like herbs have a long history of culinary use but are rarely grown as garden herbs.

Fat hen is an annual that thrives in both gardens and uncultivated ground. It grows up to 90 cm (3 ft) high, and bears diamond-shaped leaves on upright stems. The pale green flowers are carried in upright spikes from the tip of the stems and in the leaf axils. Fat hen has been used as a food plant since prehistoric times and was ousted as a staple vegetable only with the introduction of spinach. In fact, the leaves contain more iron, vitamin B_1 and protein than spinach.

Good King Henry, a 30 to 75 cm (1 to 2½ ft) tall perennial, is a pot herb; its large, bright green, arrowhead-shaped leaves, 5 to 11 cm (2 to 4½ in.) long, are cooked as a substitute for its relative, spinach. In addition, the young shoots of the plant can be cut and eaten like asparagus when they are about the thickness of a finger; in Britain they are sometimes known as "Lincoln Asparagus".

HOW TO GROW. Fat hen and Good King Henry grow throughout Europe. Both flourish in any kind of well-drained soil, but Good King Henry is better grown in partial shade. To propagate Good King Henry from seed, sow the seeds in spring, then thin the seedlings, which will be slow to appear, to stand 23 to 30 cm (9 to 12 in.) apart. Feed during the growing season with a general fertilizer; new plants can be obtained more easily by dividing the root clumps of mature plants. Until the plants are three years old, cut only a few leaves at a time to avoid injuring the plant. They taste best in the spring. If early shoots are to be cut like asparagus, cover the plant roots with 10 to 12.5 cm (4 to 5 in.) of leaf-mould or garden compost in the autumn, shielding them from light to ensure that the tender spring shoots will be blanched white. Cut the shoots off just beneath the soil's surface.

To grow fat hen, collect the seeds in summer from wild plants and store in an airtight container in a cool, dry place. Sow in early autumn or in spring. Harvest the young leaves for cooking from early summer onwards.

CHRYSANTHEMUM
C. balsamita (costmary, aleçost, Bible leaf); *C. parthenium*, also called *Pyrethrum parthenium*, *Matricaria eximia* (feverfew)

The fragrance of mint, lemon and balsam seems pleasingly combined in the oval leaves of costmary, a sprawling perennial growing 60 to 90 cm (2 to 3 ft) tall. The dried leaves add fragrance to potpourris and serve as a fixative to preserve the other scents. When young, the leaves can be included in salads, though they taste rather spicy, and they can also be used to flavour soups, meat and poultry stuffings. They were once used as a flavouring for ale, hence the name alecost. The herbalist Gerard noted the beneficial effects of a conserve made from costmary leaves and sugar, which "doth warm and dry the braine and openeth the stoppings of the same". Most of the 12.5 to 20 cm (5 to 8 in.) long leaves spread from the base of the plant. In late summer, tiny, bright yellow button flowers appear on the stems.

Feverfew is grown in gardens as a decorative plant for its attractive leaves and long blooming season but, on a commercial scale, the dried flower heads are used in medicinal compounds; a related species is used in the manufacture of the insecticide pyrethrum. Feverfew is a perennial, but as it is rather short-lived it is often grown as an annual. It reaches a height of 60 cm (2 ft) with erect stems clothed with deeply cut, pale green leaves that curl

COSTMARY
Chrysanthemum balsamita

delicately at the edges; they have a pleasant aroma. From midsummer until the frost, feverfew produces an abundance of 2 cm ($\frac{3}{4}$ in.), button flowers, golden in colour and surrounded by white ray florets. There are several garden cultivars with single or double, pure white or yellow flowers; they all bloom in their first year.

HOW TO GROW. Costmary is fully hardy and grows throughout Europe. It needs full sun and dry, well-drained soil. It can be grown in partial shade but then rarely flowers. Because costmary spreads rapidly from underground stolons or runners, it is easier to start new plants from root divisions. It rarely sets seeds. Set young plants in the garden in early spring placing them 60 to 90 cm (2 to 3 ft) apart to allow for their sprawling growth. To grow costmary indoors, transplant a root division into a proprietary potting compost in a 10 to 15 cm (4 to 6 in.) pot. Keep it on a sunny window sill. The soil should be moist but not soggy. If grown indoors it seldom becomes more than 45 cm ($1\frac{1}{2}$ ft) high.

Although fully hardy in Europe, feverfew lasts only one or two years and is better grown as an annual. It grows best in light, well-drained soil and in full sun. Sow seeds outdoors in spring, or in autumn in mild districts, and cover them lightly with soil. Thin the seedlings to stand about 25 cm (10 in.) apart. For earlier flowering, seeds can also be sown indoors in pots or seed trays in late winter and the seedlings planted out in mid-spring. Feverfew makes a good indoor pot plant; sow the seeds in late summer or early autumn and pot the seedlings up in a proprietary potting compost. Given four or five hours of direct light a day, regular watering and a fortnightly feed when the first flower buds appear, the plants will bloom in late winter and early spring.

Illustration by Pamela Freeman

FEVERFEW
Chrysanthemum parthenium

CHRYSANTHEMUM VULGARE See *Tanacetum*

CICHORIUM
C. intybus (chicory, succory)

Chicory is best known for the flavour of its ground and roasted taproot, which is used as a substitute for, or an addition to, coffee blends. The large, deeply serrated leaves on the lower half of the stems are excellent as salad greens, and they may also be cooked like spinach. In the herb garden, throughout the summer, the 90 cm (3 ft) tall perennial produces lovely light blue, daisy-like flowers along its lanky stems. The blossoms open and close like clockwork, morning and evening; in fact, their timing is so reliable that the botanist Linnaeus included chicory in a floral clock that marked the hours with blooms.

HOW TO GROW. Chicory, fully hardy in Europe, needs full sun and will grow in almost any soil. In fact, in some areas it is a roadside weed. Turn over the soil to a depth of at least 30 cm (1 ft) to accommodate the long taproot, and dig in generous amounts of manure or garden compost. Sow the seeds in early spring, covering them with 6 to 12 mm ($\frac{1}{4}$ to $\frac{1}{2}$ in.) of soil. When the first true leaves appear, thin the seedlings to stand about 30 cm (1 ft) apart. Chicory does not flower the first year, but blossoms appear during the second and succeeding years.

In order to reduce the bitterness of the tight-pressed leaves, called chicons, it is necessary to blanch them. In the autumn of the first year, just before the ground has frozen, trim back the top growth to ground level, dig up the root and bury it at least 25 cm (10 in.) deep in a large box or deep pot of potting compost which is then placed in a cool, dark place. Keep the compost moist but not soggy, and in three or four weeks a huge, tightly curled bud of creamy-

CHICORY
Cichorium intybus

CALAMONDIN ORANGE
Citrus microcarpa

CORIANDER
Coriandrum sativum

white foliage will sprout from the top of the root; this part may be cooked whole or separated into leaves for use as a green in salads.

CITRUS
C. microcarpa, also called *C. mitis* (calamondin orange)

This miniature fruit tree, a sub-tropical evergreen native to the Philippines, is becoming increasingly popular as an ornamental house plant. When tub grown it rarely reaches a height of more than 60 cm (2 ft), and can be kept inside all year round or it can be moved outside during the warmer months. Intermittently throughout the year, calamondin orange produces a succession of fragrant, 8 to 25 mm ($\frac{1}{3}$ to 1 in.), white flowers followed by fruit that requires nearly a year to ripen. The ripened fruit, about 2.5 cm (1 in.) in diameter, is edible, albeit somewhat tart; it makes a good marmalade.

HOW TO GROW. In Europe, except for hot Mediterranean areas, this citrus must be treated as a pot plant and can be kept outdoors only during the summer months. It can be started from seed, but is best propagated from stem cuttings taken from midsummer to late autumn. For the most abundant flowers and fruit, place the potted plant in a position that receives at least four hours of direct sunlight a day, and has night temperatures of 10° to 13°C (50° to 55°F) and day temperatures of 20° to 22°C (68° to 72°F). Calamondin orange is damaged by overwatering, but the roots must never be allowed to become completely dry. It thrives in a moist atmosphere and should be set on a tray of pebbles that is kept filled with water to supply the necessary humidity. If a plant becomes too large, cut it back as severely as necessary; pruning is best done in the early spring. Calamondin orange, like other citrus species, is vulnerable to attack from mealy bugs and spider mites. To control the insects, wash the plants with a forceful spray of water and, if this is not effective, spray them with malathion every 10 days as necessary—but do not spray with malathion indoors.

COCHLEARIA See *Armoracia*

CORIANDRUM
C. sativum (coriander, Chinese parsley)

Coriander is one of the ancient herbs and has been used for thousands of years in both cooking and medicine. The aromatic, sweet-tasting seeds are used in baking, liqueurs, in pickling spice mixtures and as an essential ingredient of curry spices. The fresh green, dainty, parsley-like leaves are a common flavouring in Indian, Pakistani, Chinese, Middle Eastern and Latin American cooking. The plant is an annual that becomes 30 to 60 cm (1 to 2 ft) tall. In early summer, the delicately branched stems bear lacy flower heads of tiny, white, pale pink or lavender blossoms; these then ripen into small, light-brown fruit, or seed pods, about 3 mm ($\frac{1}{8}$ in.) in diameter.

HOW TO GROW. Coriander grows throughout Europe, but does best in its native southern Europe. It requires full sun and will grow in any well-drained soil of average richness. Sow seeds in the late spring, when danger of frost has passed, in a site protected from the wind—coriander becomes top-heavy and tends to blow over. Sow seeds 12 to 18 mm ($\frac{1}{2}$ to $\frac{3}{4}$ in.) deep. When seedlings are 5 to 7.5 cm (2 to 3 in.) tall, thin them to stand 20 to 25 cm (8 to 10 in.) apart. Plants started in spring will bloom about nine weeks later and produce seeds in late summer. If the pods are allowed to ripen on the plant, coriander will seed itself.

Coriander leaves can be cut for seasoning as soon as the plant is 10 to 15 cm (4 to 6 in.) tall; they are always used fresh. Harvest the seeds as soon as the pods are light brown. Cut off the entire plant with the seed pods still attached and carefully drop it into a paper bag; dry in a warm, dark place. Shake the dried pods inside the bag to remove them from the stems, then rub them between the palms of the hands to split the pods and remove the seeds. Store whole seeds in an airtight container; once ground they quickly lose their flavour.

CRITHMUM
C. maritimum (samphire, sea fennel)

Samphire, a salt-resistant perennial, is native to areas where few other plants survive, in the high winds and sea spray of the beaches and coastal cliffs of southern and western Europe. Its rubbery, 2.5 cm (1 in.) leaves are divided into narrow, spear-shaped leaflets that are salty, aromatic and rich in iodine; they are usually pickled and are a popular accompaniment to drinks in Mediterranean countries. Sometimes the leaves are added to salads or cooked like spinach.

The plant reaches a height of 23 to 30 cm (9 to 12 in.). In early summer samphire produces small clusters of yellow flower heads.

HOW TO GROW. Samphire needs full sun and well-drained gravelly or sandy soil. It will grow in sheltered coastal regions of Britain, but does best on the Atlantic seaboard and along the Mediterranean. Sow seeds in early spring, as soon as the soil can be prepared, and thin the plants to stand 45 cm (1½ ft) apart. Samphire can also be propagated by root division in the spring or from stem cuttings. If seaweed is available, it can be used as a mulch round plants; or you can dig in a spoonful of table salt once or twice during the growing season.

CROCUS
C. sativus (saffron crocus)

This autumn-flowering, bulbous plant has been culti-vated since ancient times for saffron, the flavouring derived from its flower stigma, a substance so rare it was long considered a prerogative of royalty. It takes roughly 8,000 flowers to produce 100 grams (3½ oz) of dried saffron. Nero ordered saffron to be sprinkled on the streets of Rome for his entry into the city, and medieval scribes burnished saffron upon foil as a substitute for gold in illuminated manuscripts. Commercially cultivated in southern Europe, the Levant, Iran and China as a colouring and flavouring agent for food, the plant is now grown chiefly for garden decoration and is prized because it blooms in the autumn when most flowers are gone. From the 14th to the end of the 19th century the saffron industry in Britain was centred in Saffron Walden, in Essex. The saffron crocus should not be confused with the other autumn-flowering bulb, the meadow saffron (*Colchicum autumnale*) which is extremely poisonous.

Saffron crocus grows from a small, brown, bulbous corm, about 2.5 cm (1 in.) in diameter, from which rise several stems 7.5 to 10 cm (3 to 4 in.) high. Each stem pro-duces a single, sweetly scented, chalice-shaped bud that opens to a star-shaped flower about 6 cm (2½ in.) across; it stays open at night as well as during the day. Grass-like leaves, about 20 cm (8 in.) long, appear before the flowers in the autumn and stay green through the winter, dying back in late spring.

HOW TO GROW. Saffron crocus grows in all parts of Europe but does best in temperate regions where winters are cold.

SAMPHIRE
Crithmum maritimum

SAFFRON CROCUS
Crocus sativus

Illustration by Pamela Freeman

CUMIN
Cuminum cyminum

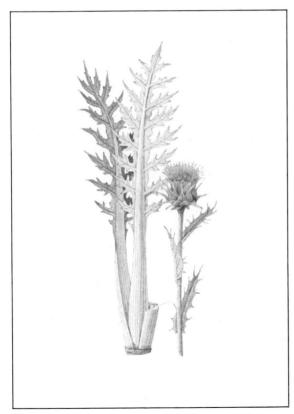

CARDOON
Cynara cardunculus

It will tolerate light shade, but prefers full sun in a sheltered position and light, rich, well-drained soil. Plant corms as early as they are available, placing them in groups 5 to 15 cm (2 to 6 in.) apart; cover them with 5 to 10 cm (2 to 4 in.) of soil. Left undisturbed, they multiply naturally and increase in beauty from one year to the next, though they can be dug up and divided in early summer every three or four years, if desired. Saffron crocus is sterile, and can be propagated only by proliferation of the underground corms.

CUMINUM
C. cyminum, also called *C. odorum* (cumin)

Cumin is a Mediterranean annual cultivated for its pungent seeds, which have been prized as a condiment since Biblical times and are today an ingredient of Indian, North African and Mexican cooking. It is highly aromatic and spicy, and the dried seeds are used, whole or ground, to flavour meat and curry dishes. The plant's diminutive size, 10 to 15 cm (4 to 6 in.), and spidery, deep-green foliage make it a useful edging plant. The mauve or white blossoms are tiny, but mature into yellowish-brown seeds, about 6 mm ($\frac{1}{4}$ in.) long, which must be dried to develop their distinctive and pungent flavour; the seeds resemble caraway, but the flavour is totally different.

HOW TO GROW. Cumin needs three to four months of warm summer weather to mature. It is grown successfully only in southern Europe and needs full sun and a well-drained soil of average fertility. In mild regions, sow seeds in early spring indoors, using three or four seeds to a 10 cm (4 in.) pot of a proprietary seed compost. Transplant the clump of seedlings outdoors without disturbing the roots when night temperatures fall no lower than 12°C (54°F), setting the clumps 10 cm (4 in.) apart. In frost-free regions, such as along the Mediterranean, sow seeds outdoors when warm weather arrives. Keep the soil moist in hot, dry weather. Pick the seeds when the pods turn brown. Let them dry completely; then rub the seed heads to free seeds and store these in an airtight container.

CYNARA
C. cardunculus (cardoon, wild artichoke)

The cardoon, a near relative of the globe artichoke, is a perennial grown for its edible, celery-like leaf-stalks, though it also has decorative thistle-like, blue or purple flowers, 12 to 50 mm ($\frac{1}{2}$ to 2 in.) across, that bloom in late summer. The pale, ribbed stalks, which may grow up to 90 cm (3 ft) tall, produce thick, green, spiky leaves with fuzzy, white undersides.

HOW TO GROW. Cardoons are perennial in warm, frost-free regions, but they are more usually grown as an annual vegetable crop. They do best in a rich, moist soil and in full sun. Sow seeds in the spring when all danger of frost is past, or start them in pots indoors in mid-spring. If you are planting cardoons for eating, sow seeds or set seedlings at the bottom of a 30 cm (1 ft) deep trench that will later be filled in during the blanching process. Cover seeds with 2.5 cm (1 in.) of soil, and thin or transplant seedlings to stand about 60 to 90 cm (2 to 3 ft) apart. Plants grown for eating are blanched, or whitened, by shielding them from light for a month before harvesting. Tie the stalks together and pile earth around them to the point where the leaves begin. Choose a dry day so that the inner leaves are not wet or they will rot. Plants grown as ornamentals should be cut back after flowering in the autumn, and protected from frost with a mulch of bracken or leaves. Or lift the roots and store in a cold frame over winter for planting outdoors in spring when all danger of frost is past.

Cardoon may seed itself, or its seeds can be harvested for sowing the following spring. New plants can also be propagated from side shoots that develop when the older plants are cut back for the winter.

CYTISUS

C. scoparius, also called *Sarothamnus scoparius* (broom, cat's peas, golden chair, lady's slipper)

This hardy shrub is native to Europe where it grows wild in heathland tracts and similar dry places, flowering with a brilliant golden extravagance in spring. The stiff, bright green stems were formerly tied together in bunches and used to sweep out houses, hence the common name. The tiny, yellow flower buds can be used fresh in mixed salads or pickled in the same way as nasturtium buds and seeds and used as a substitute for capers. In country districts, the fully opened flowers are also sometimes used, together with other ingredients, to make a golden-coloured wine.

Broom grows up to 2.4 metres (8 ft) high with an equal spread. Although it is deciduous, the fresh green stems give it an evergreen appearance in winter. The stems are sparsely clothed with small, green leaves, and in early summer are almost hidden by cascades of golden-yellow, pea-like flowers. There are numerous cultivars in shades of yellow, white, orange, pink, crimson and purple and also bicoloured forms.

HOW TO GROW. Brooms are fully hardy in all parts of Europe and thrive in ordinary, preferably poor and dry but well-drained, soil in full sun. They are difficult to transplant, so buy nursery-grown container plants where possible and set them out in early autumn or in spring. Brooms are easily increased from seeds sown in midspring, but named cultivars do not come true to colour and must be multiplied by stem cuttings taken in late summer or early autumn and rooted in peat and sand in a cold frame. Brooms tend to become leggy and bare at the base unless they are pruned annually after flowering: cut back by half the shoots that have flowered, but be careful not to cut into the old wood.

D

DICTAMNUS

D. albus, also called *D. fraxinella* (gas plant, fraxinella, false dittany, burning bush)

The curious common names of this perennial, gas plant and burning bush, come from the fact that in hot, dry, calm weather it produces an oily vapour that sometimes bursts into flame when ignited; this flash of fire does not hurt the plant. Quirky behaviour aside, the gas plant is grown for its strong, lemony fragrance and its attractive flowers and ornamental seed pods, both of which are popular for indoor flower arrangements.

The gas plant is an erect, bushy plant, 60 cm (2 ft) or more high and wide, with a long life expectancy: in some well-established gardens there are gas plants more than 50 years old. The plant's shiny, dark green, leathery leaves are composed of oval leaflets arranged in pairs. In early summer, delicate white flower spikes flutter 25 to 30 cm (10 to 12 in.) above the foliage; the individual flowers are 2.5 to 5 cm (1 to 2 in.) across, and from the base of each blossom project reddish-purple filaments tipped by green anthers. The flowers do not appear until the plant is three or four years old, but subsequently they grow more abundant each year.

HOW TO GROW. The gas plant, hardy throughout Europe,

BROOM
Cytisus scoparius

Illustration by Mary Ann Hodson—The Garden Studio

GAS PLANT
Dictamnus albus

TEASEL
Dipsacus sylvestris

prefers full sun but will tolerate partial shade. It thrives in any well-drained, moderately rich, light-textured soil. Because it is long lived, dig the soil deeply before planting and add compost or moss peat to prepare for the potentially far-reaching root system. Grow gas plants from nursery stock or propagate them from seed, but, if growing them from seed, do not expect blossoms until the third or fourth year. Set the young plants 1 to 1.2 metres (3 to 4 ft) apart in their permanent site. The gas plant requires little care; its foliage dies to the ground each autumn but the roots send up new growth in the spring.

DIPSACUS
D. sylvestris, also called *D. fullonum* (teasel)

Teasel is a 1.5 to 1.8 metre (5 to 6 ft) tall biennial cultivated for its prickly, oval heads, which are used in dried flower arrangements, and for its seeds, which are an ingredient of bird food. At one time, weavers used the teasel's comb-like heads to raise, or tease, the pile of wool. In the first year, the plant produces only a low rosette of coarse, tooth-edged leaves. In the second year, prickly stems rise from the rosette, bearing pairs of hairy, lanceshaped leaves, 15 to 50 cm (6 to 20 in.) long, covered underneath with bristly spines. During the summer, the stems are capped by flower heads composed of tiny, lilac florets that begin to bloom in the centre of the head, gradually spreading upwards and downwards. In late summer, the flower heads begin to turn brown and are filled with dark, rod-shaped seeds.

HOW TO GROW. Teasel can be cultivated in all parts of Europe. It grows best in full sun but will tolerate partial shade; it thrives in almost any soil. Sow seeds in late spring where plants are to grow; when seedlings are 5 to 7.5 cm (2 to 3 in.) tall, thin them to 60 cm (2 ft) apart. If not controlled, teasel spreads by seeding itself and is difficult to eradicate. Cut the flower heads before seeds ripen to keep it in bounds. If you are harvesting teasel for dried arrangements, cut them just after seed pods have formed and dry either in an upright position or by hanging in bunches upside down.

F

FILIPENDULA
F. vulgaris, also called *F. hexapetala*, *Spiraea filipendula* and *Ulmaria filipendula* (meadowsweet, dropwort)

Sweet-smelling meadowsweet was the favourite herb of Queen Elizabeth I for masking the odours of unaired rooms. She "did more desire it than any other sweet herb to strew her chambers withal", according to the Elizabethan herbalist John Parkinson. Meadowsweet was also used to flavour ales and homemade wines and jams. The dried flowers were sometimes used for herbal teas and thought to be remedial in treating kidney disorders. Today, this hardy perennial is cultivated as a handsome, lacy addition to a border. The plant grows 38 to 45 cm ($1\frac{1}{4}$ to $1\frac{1}{2}$ ft) tall and has fern-like leaves, 15 to 50 cm (6 to 20 in.) long, in a rosette, from the centre of which the flower stems rise. Each stem is capped in early spring with airy clusters of fragrant, white flowers up to 20 cm (8 in.) across.

HOW TO GROW. Meadowsweet, found wild in temperate Europe, grows in full sun or light shade and does best in wet soil, although it tolerates dry soil. Any garden soil enriched with compost, moss peat or manure is suitable. Sow seeds in the autumn in seed trays and keep them in a cold frame through the winter. In the spring, transplant the seedlings to the garden, spacing them 30 cm (1 ft) apart; they will produce foliage the first year and flowers each

MEADOWSWEET
Filipendula vulgaris

year thereafter. Meadowsweet can be left in place indefinitely. In addition to being grown from seed, it can be propagated by dividing root clumps in early spring. The double-flowered form of meadowsweet, *F. vulgaris* 'Flore Pleno', can be increased only by root division.

FOENICULUM
F. vulgare, also called *F. officinale* (fennel); *F. vulgare* var. *dulce*, also called *F. dulce* (Florence fennel, finocchio)

Fennel, a graceful and bushy perennial, is one of the oldest known culinary herbs. Its anise-flavoured leaves and seeds are highly valued in fish cookery and as a flavouring in accompanying sauces; the finely chopped leaves can also be added to soups and salad dressing and the seeds are used to flavour pickles and vinegars. It grows 1 to 1.8 metres (3 to 6 ft) tall, with a thick, glossy main stem and feathery leaves; in summer these are topped by clusters of tiny, yellow flowers. By late summer the flower clusters begin to droop under the weight of their brown, ribbed seeds, almost 12 mm ($\frac{1}{2}$ in.) long, which give off a strong, sweet scent.

Fennel's smaller cousin Florence fennel, sometimes known as finocchio, is about 60 cm (2 ft) tall and grown not for its leaves or seeds but for its bulbous leaf base, which varies from pale green to white and has a delicate anise flavour. It is a popular cooked vegetable and is also used raw in salads.

HOW TO GROW. Fennel, though a hardy perennial, is usually grown as an annual. It does best in full sun, in any garden soil with a pH of 6.0 to 8.0, supplemented with a general fertilizer at the amount of 85 grams (3 oz) to 3 metres (10 ft) of row. Florence fennel requires the same conditions, but, in addition, the soil should be enriched with garden compost.

Sow fennel seeds in early spring if you want to harvest seeds as well as leaves. If you grow the plant for its leaves alone, the seeds can be sown continuously at 10-day intervals until summer, assuring a continuous fresh supply. Be sure not to grow fennel and dill close together, since the two cross-pollinate. Fennel can also be propagated by root division in the early spring.

Sow Florence fennel in mid-spring; harvest the thick bulbous stem in late summer and early autumn. Lightly cover seeds of both species with a thin layer of soil, and when the seedlings are 5 cm (2 in.) high, thin or transplant them to stand about 30 cm (1 ft) apart. Unless it is growing near a fence or a wall, fennel may need to be staked when it gets tall to protect it from strong winds. Fennel flower heads should be cut before they bloom if the plant is being grown for its leaves alone; this encourages greater leaf growth especially if it is grown as a perennial. The flower heads of Florence fennel should also be cut off before they bloom to encourage the development of a thicker base. When the bulbous base is about the size of an egg, cover it with soil halfway up to blanch it. The base will be ready for harvesting in August and September.

Fennel leaves can be harvested continuously from the time the flower heads form until just before the first frost. Use them fresh; or dry them in the shade and store them in an airtight container. Harvest fennel seeds when they ripen in the autumn and spread them in a thin layer on a screen in the shade to dry, turning them often.

FRAGARIA
F. vesca (alpine strawberry)

The delicious strawberry is well known to every gardener; many European gardeners devote a sunny bed in

FENNEL
Foeniculum vulgare

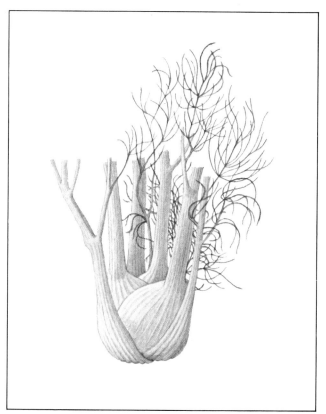

FLORENCE FENNEL
Foeniculum vulgare var. *dulce*

ALPINE STRAWBERRY
Fragaria vesca

WOODRUFF
Galium odoratum

the vegetable and fruit garden to the cultivation of this fruit. Modern cultivars make large, bushy plants, but the pretty little alpine strawberry is ideal for edging a herb garden. It does not produce runners and therefore does not exhaust itself as quickly as the large-berried plants. Alpine strawberries, although perennial, will fruit the same year when raised from seed; the cultivar 'Baron Solemacher' produces heavy crops of small, but extremely sweet berries over many weeks in summer; in warm summers it often continues to berry well into autumn.

HOW TO GROW. Alpine strawberries grow in all parts of temperate and southern Europe. They thrive in well-drained soil rich in organic matter, and in full sun. Plants can be raised from seed sown indoors in peat pots in early spring, hardened off in a cold frame and planted out in late spring about 30 cm (1 ft) apart. Plants can also be bought from nurseries and set out at the same distances. On young plants, remove the first flowers that appear in spring to encourage a second blooming and fruits to harvest in late summer and autumn. Strawberries are surface rooting, so be careful when hoeing to remove weeds; it is a good idea to mulch the plants with garden compost or leaf-mould which will keep the soil cool and free of weeds and give the plants extra nourishment.

G

GALIUM

G. odoratum, also called *Asperula odorata* (woodruff, sweet woodruff); *G. verum* (lady's bedstraw, curdwort, cheese rennet)

Woodruff, a low-growing perennial, 15 to 20 cm (6 to 8 in.) high, is noted for having leaves that smell of new-mown hay—but only when dried. The leaves are used to flavour wine punches, especially May wine, and they are also used in herb teas and sachets. Woodruff was once used as a strewing herb, releasing its sweet fragrance as it was walked upon. The plant has shiny, oblong leaves growing in delicate whorls around the stem. In late April and May it is capped with clusters of tiny, white, star-shaped flowers that are excellent for cutting. An attractive ground cover suitable for shady areas, it spreads rapidly from creeping, above-ground roots called stolons. Its seeds are thickly covered with hairy bristles that often attach themselves to the fur and feathers of animals and birds.

Lady's bedstraw is a 30 to 90 cm (1 to 3 ft) tall, wild plant whose springy stems and leaves give the plant an airy appearance; they were once used to stuff mattresses and, like woodruff, smell of new-mown hay. Mossy leaves, 2.5 to 5 cm (1 to 2 in.) long, circle the stem in groups of six or eight. From spring to late summer the plant blooms in 7.5 to 10 cm (3 to 4 in.) clusters of tiny, yellow flowers. Formerly a yellow dye was extracted from lady's bedstraw but its main use was in cheesemaking because the leaf juices set up a chemical reaction similar to rennet.

HOW TO GROW. Woodruff grows in all parts of Europe, although it does not thrive so well in hot southern parts. It needs shade and a loose, moist, acid soil—pH 4.5 to 5.5—supplemented with leaf-mould. In its natural European habitat it is a woodland plant and in gardens it will turn brown and die if exposed to full sun and dry soil. Seeds germinate well if fresh, but old seeds may be in the ground about a year before they germinate; for this reason root divisions or stem cuttings are the common methods of propagation. Take cuttings from mature plants in the spring or autumn and set them in wet sand; they will root in three weeks or less. Divide the roots in the spring or early autumn and set the root clumps in the ground 23 to

30 cm (9 to 12 in.) apart. Soak the soil well after planting and keep it moist but not soggy.

Lady's bedstraw, commonly found growing wild throughout Europe, does well in sun or partial shade and in almost any soil. Suitable for large rock gardens, it is a sprawling plant, but can be staked if upright growth is desired. It will seed itself, but is most easily propagated from root divisions planted early in the spring, 30 cm (1 ft) apart. Root clumps should be divided every two or three years in the spring.

Woodruff is harvested in late spring, just before it blooms or while it is still in flower, when its scent is most intense. Dry in a cool, dark place so that the leaves retain some greenness, then strip the leaves from the stems and store them in an airtight container.

Woodruff can also be potted in the summer and taken indoors. It requires a moist but well-drained acid soil, cool conditions and at least five hours of filtered sunlight a day.

GLYCYRRHIZA
G. glabra (liquorice, Spanish juice, black sugar)

This hardy perennial is cultivated on a large commercial scale in southern Europe and Asia for its roots, which yield the liquorice used in confectionery and medicine as well as a food flavouring. It was one of the ancient herbs, growing wild in Palestine at the time of Christ and probably even then popular among children, who chew the sweet, dried, straw-yellow root or the hard, black sticks that are produced from the concentrated root juice.

Liquorice grows 90 cm (3 ft) high, and can be invasive in gardens because of its spreading underground roots. The oblong leaves are composed of pairs of mid-green leaflets that are sticky on the undersides. From late spring and throughout summer the plant bears purplish-blue, bean-like flowers in short spikes from the tops of the stems and the leaf axils.

HOW TO GROW. Liquorice is fully hardy in Europe although it grows best for commercial purposes in Mediterranean climates. It thrives in rich, moist soil and in full sun. New plants can be raised from seed, but it is easier to divide the creeping roots and replant the divisions. In autumn cut down the foliage to just above ground level and at the same time chop off some of the spreading roots with a sharp spade. Roots for liquorice are ready for harvesting after three years of growth.

H

HELIOTROPIUM
H. arborescens, also called *H. peruvianum* and *H. corymbosum* (common heliotrope, cherry pie)

Common heliotrope, a tender perennial shrub that was used in the preparation of certain perfumeries, is usually treated as an annual plant for summer flower beds and window boxes. It normally grows as a bush 15 to 30 cm (6 to 12 in.) tall, but by trimming off the shoots along the central stem you can train it into a standard form. Its tiny, 3 to 6 mm ($\frac{1}{8}$ to $\frac{1}{4}$ in.) flowers have an appealing vanilla scent; they bloom densely in 5 to 10 cm (2 to 4 in.) clusters from early summer until autumn. The oblong, pointed leaves, 2.5 to 7.5 cm (1 to 3 in.) long, are wrinkled and hairy, with prominent veins.

HOW TO GROW. Common heliotrope grows as a half-hardy bedding plant in temperate Europe, and in mild frost-free regions as a perennial. It can be treated as a perennial anywhere if it is planted in a pot and taken indoors during the winter. It does well in any garden soil in full sun or light shade, but the soil should be kept moist. To grow it from seed, sow the seeds indoors 12 mm ($\frac{1}{2}$ in.) apart in

LADY'S BEDSTRAW
Galium verum

COMMON HELIOTROPE
Heliotropium arborescens

HYSSOP
Hyssopus officinalis

ELECAMPANE
Inula helenium

trays in late winter. Transfer the seedlings to the open ground when night temperatures are consistently mild, setting the plants 30 cm (1 ft) apart. Common heliotrope can also be propagated from stem cuttings (choose young, flowerless side shoots taken in summer and overwintered indoors). Grown indoors, common heliotrope needs at least four hours of direct sunlight a day. Keep the soil moist, but not soggy, and fertilize the plant at two-week intervals with a liquid house-plant fertilizer used at half the recommended strength.

HYSSOPUS
H. officinalis (hyssop)

Once popular as a household strewing herb, fragrant when walked upon, hyssop was also used in medicinal infusions and as a flavouring for meats; today, it is valued for its decorative qualities. It is a shrub-like, semi-evergreen perennial, 45 to 60 cm (1½ to 2 ft) tall, that is often used as a low hedge. Throughout the summer, clusters of tiny blossoms of blue, pink or white grow in whorls around the plant's flower spikes. Scented hyssop blossoms attract bees and butterflies. The narrow green leaves are aromatic and can be used in the young stage to add minty flavours to salads and cooked vegetables.

HOW TO GROW. Hyssop grows in all parts of Europe though less successfully in cold northern areas. It is native to southern Europe, and grows in sun or partial shade, and will thrive in any well-drained soil. Sow seeds 6 mm (¼ in.) deep in spring or autumn and thin seedlings to stand 30 cm (1 ft) apart; for faster results, start with nursery stock. Hyssop is fairly hardy and its roots seldom need winter protection, but the stems should be cut back to the ground each autumn or spring to encourage new growth. After three or four years, plants grow woody and produce less foliage; to renew a sparse hedge, divide the roots of mature plants in spring or autumn or start new plants from seed.

I

INULA
I. helenium (elecampane, horseheal)

Elecampane is grown in some regions for its bitter, aromatic root, which is used as a flavouring in liqueurs, country medicines or in confectionery, but its bright yellow flowers, resembling miniature sunflowers, make it a handsome background plant for the garden. It is a hardy perennial, 1.2 to 1.8 metres (4 to 6 ft) tall, with coarse, deeply veined leaves, downy on the underside; leaves at the base of the plant may be more than 45 cm (1½ ft) long and 20 cm (8 in.) wide. The flowers are 7.5 to 10 cm (3 to 4 in.) across and bloom from midsummer to late summer.

HOW TO GROW. Native to Europe, elecampane grows wild in most regions. It will grow in full sun or partial shade and thrives in almost any moist soil. Sow seeds outdoors in the spring or autumn. When plants are 5 to 7.5 cm (2 to 3 in.) tall, thin or transplant them to stand 60 to 120 cm (2 to 4 ft) apart. Elecampane can also be propagated from root divisions in the spring or autumn. Every three years the plants should be renewed by dividing their roots.

IRIS
I. germanica var. *florentina* (orris, flag iris, Florentine iris)

Orris, a type of the ordinary blue garden iris, is grown for its violet-scented root, which is used in dried and powdered form as a fixative to reinforce other fragrances. An ingredient in many perfumes, it can be added to sachets and potpourris, but it must be used with caution, since some people are allergic to it. Its flower inspired the fleur-de-lis of French heraldry.

The stiff, sword-shaped leaves grow 45 to 60 cm (1½ to 2 ft) high. Large, white flowers with lavender veins and yellow beards bloom in mid to late spring.

HOW TO GROW. Orris is native to the Mediterranean regions, but grows throughout Europe. A perennial, it needs full sun and will grow in any well-drained soil, even dry and gravelly soils. It grows from rhizomes planted at any time the soil can be worked, but preferably in early summer. Place the rhizomes horizontally so that their tops lie just at the surface of the soil, 30 to 45 cm (1 to 1½ ft) apart, with the stubby anchoring roots pointing downwards. The plants will produce foliage that will die down in the autumn and flowers will appear the following spring. When the plants finish flowering, cut back the flower stalks to discourage seed production. Orris roots multiply rapidly and can be dug up, divided and transplanted or harvested every three or four years in early summer immediately after flowering.

Harvest orris roots by digging up, washing and peeling them; then put them in the sun to dry. Store the roots in a dry place for one or two years to develop their characteristic violet fragrance. After this storage period, they are ready to be ground into powder.

ISATIS
I. tinctoria (woad, dyer's-weed)

Woad is a yellow-flowered member of the mustard family, once famous for the blue dye extracted from its leaves and used by ancient Britons to paint their bodies. Today, both the flower panicles and the pendulous seeds are popular for fresh flower arrangements. It is a biennial, forming a low rosette of oval leaves in the first year of growth. The following spring, sturdy stems rise 45 to 120 cm (1½ to 4 ft) tall bearing lance-shaped leaves, which graduate from a maximum of about 10 cm (4 in.) long at the base to 4 cm (1½ in.) at the top; the leaves have the blue-green colour of broccoli leaves. Woad blooms in early summer in panicles that spread as much as 60 cm (2 ft) wide. The golden-yellow flowers are followed by black seeds that hang from the stems for several weeks.

HOW TO GROW. Woad is hardy in all parts of Europe and grows in partial shade or full sun, in any rich, well-drained garden soil. Sow seeds in the late summer so that the plants will be well established before winter. Thin or transplant seedlings when they are 5 to 7.5 cm (2 to 3 in.) high, spacing them 15 to 30 cm (6 to 12 in.) apart. Seedlings are best transplanted in the early spring when the ground is moist. If the seed heads of the plant are cut before ripening, woad acts as a short-lived perennial but if it is allowed to blossom normally it will reseed itself.

J

JASMINUM
J. officinale (jasmine, common jasmine, white jasmine, tea jasmine)

The fragrance of jasmine on a summer night has inspired poets to verse, and its petals are a mainstay of the perfume industry. In its native Kashmir it is a semi-evergreen climber, reaching a height of 9 to 12 metres (30 to 40 ft); under ideal conditions it can reach similar heights in gardens, but is generally kept pruned to a more manageable size and is treated as a shrub. Jasmine leaves grow in pairs, with each leaf made up of three to seven leaflets that range in size from 1.2 to 6 cm (½ to 2½ in.) long; the snow-white, sweetly scented flowers bloom in clusters

ORRIS
Iris germanica var. *florentina*

WOAD
Isatis tinctoria

115

JASMINE
Jasminum officinale

JUNIPER
Juniperus communis

Illustration by Mary Ann Hodson—The Garden Studio

at the ends of new growth throughout summer.

HOW TO GROW. Jasmine is fully hardy in all parts of Europe; in northern regions it is sometimes cut down by frost during very severe winters, but usually springs again from the base. It does well in full sun or partial shade in any garden soil. Plant young container-grown plants in autumn or spring. Prune only after flowering, because the flowers appear on young branches. Propagate additional plants from 7.5 to 15 cm (3 to 6 in.) stem cuttings taken from semi-ripe wood in late summer, rooting them in moist sand and peat. Jasmine can also be grown as a house plant, and, unlike most summer-flowering plants, often continues to bloom indoors all winter long. It thrives in high humidity, night temperatures of 10° to 13°C (50° to 55°F), day temperatures above 18°C (65°F), and a rich potting soil. It requires at least four hours of direct sunlight daily. During periods of active growth, feed indoor plants with a liquid general fertilizer diluted to half the recommended strength. Do not feed during rest periods. Set pots on trays of moist pebbles indoors to supply extra humidity. Keep the soil barely damp in the winter, but water generously from March to October, keeping the soil moist but not soggy. Indoor plants may need drastic pruning; cut back straggling branches after they have flowered. The average size of indoor plants is 60 to 90 cm (2 to 3 ft), but they can grow 1.5 to 1.8 metres (5 to 6 ft) tall.

JUNIPERUS
J. communis (juniper)

The evergreen, coniferous juniper is a well-known and popular garden plant, but few people realize the value in cooking of its ripe berries. They are primarily used as a flavouring in gin, but in European cookery they are also valued for their aroma and flavour when added to marinades for meat and game, in poultry stuffings and patés. In Germany they are used to flavour sauerkraut, and juniper also combines well with other strong-flavoured herbs such as thyme, fennel and garlic. The berries can be bought dried, but for the finest flavour the ripe berries should be picked fresh when they are rich with the oil that releases the flavour. Crush them before use in a mortar and pestle.

Juniper grows as a sprawling bush, usually 1.8 metres (6 ft) or more high, with sprays of needle-like, pale green leaves each with a broad white band on the upper surface. Male and female flowers are borne on separate plants, but only the females bear fruit. The stems are heavily clothed with prickly spines and it is advisable to wear gloves when picking the berries. The fruit has a unique growth pattern and takes two to three years to ripen; it begins as a small green cone, but in the second or third year ripens to a bright blue in the autumn when it is ready for picking. One female bush will bear berries in varying stages of ripening, when they have the heavy, sweet scent of pine needles. The flavour and aroma of wild-growing junipers, especially in mountainous, sunny regions are often superior to those of the cultivated garden forms.

HOW TO GROW. Junipers are extremely hardy and tough and thrive in all parts of Europe and in any kind of soil, in sun or light shade. They grow equally well on chalky and acid, peaty soils. The plants can be increased from seeds picked out of the ripe berries in early autumn and sown at once. The seedlings will be ready for setting out in their permanent quarters after three years. For quicker results, stem cuttings can be taken in autumn and rooted in peat and sand in a cold frame. Harvest the berries as they ripen and use them when fresh. Any surplus can be dried on muslin-covered trays until shrivelled and wrinkled, but they will have less flavour than fresh berries.

L

LAMIUM
L. maculatum (spotted dead nettle, cobbler's bench)

This invasive perennial member of the mint family looks like a stinging nettle but does not sting, hence its name dead nettle. The stem is hollow and either erect or ascending from a sprawling base to a height of 15 to 60 cm ($\frac{1}{2}$ to 2 ft), depending on soil fertility and moisture. During the summer, the plant produces 2.5 to 5 cm (1 to 2 in.) terminal clusters of curious hooded blossoms about 2.5 cm (1 in.) long, white or magenta in colour. Bees are much attracted to dead nettle, which is grown today as a decorative ground cover. It is sometimes used in country districts as a vegetable for flavouring soups; the leaves are only mildly aromatic.

HOW TO GROW. Dead nettle is a common hedgerow plant in all parts of Europe; for garden decoration, the cultivated species and its cultivars are preferable. It does best in partial shade and moist soil, but will tolerate sun. Almost any soil will suit it. Sow seeds or start plants from root divisions in the spring. Space plants 30 cm (1 ft) apart. Dead nettle needs little care.

LAURUS
L. nobilis (sweet bay, bay laurel, bay leaf)

Sweet bay is an aromatic evergreen whose fragrant leaves, 2.5 to 7.5 cm (1 to 3 in.) long, are used for seasoning and are a standard ingredient of the *bouquet garni*. In its native Mediterranean soil, sweet bay grows into a towering tree, 12 to 18 metres (40 to 60 ft) high, but elsewhere it is usually a shrub, 1 to 3 metres (3 to 10 ft) tall, often grown in a large tub or pot. The shrub can be clipped into almost any shape, hence it is a favourite for topiary sculpture. Although sweet bay only occasionally blooms in northern climates, under favourable conditions it produces tiny, yellow blossoms in spring at the leaf axils, which are followed by purple-black berries on female plants.

HOW TO GROW. Except in the mild climate of southern Europe, where it grows well outdoors all year round, sweet bay is usually kept in a tub or pot, especially in frost-prone regions and while the plant is still young, so that it can be moved indoors in winter. Outdoors, it needs to be shaded from the heat of the summer sun and protected from the wind. Inside, it does best in a greenhouse with a controlled temperature of between 3° to 7°C (38° to 45°F). It can also be grown as an indoor herb plant in room temperatures ranging between 4° and 18°C (40° and 65°F), but in these conditions it needs at least four hours of direct sunlight or bright reflected light a day, or 12 hours of strong artificial light.

Start sweet bay from nursery stock planted in a proprietary potting compost; cuttings require more than a year to root and even then do not always take. Keep the soil moist in spring and moderately dry for the rest of the year; good drainage is essential. Do not feed for at least three months after planting. Then start to feed the plant twice a year, in early spring and in early summer, with any general fertilizer.

Sweet bay leaves can be used fresh or dried, and can be harvested at any time of the year. To dry the leaves, hang sprigs in a warm, dark room where the temperature does not exceed 21°C (70°F). When they are partly dry but not brittle, spread the leaves on a flat surface, cover them with a clean cloth and weight them with a board for about 10 days to flatten them. Store the flattened leaves in an airtight container. Caution: Do not confuse this laurel with mountain laurel (*Kalmia latifolia*) which has poisonous leaves.

SPOTTED DEAD NETTLE
Lamium maculatum

SWEET BAY
Laurus nobilis

FRINGED LAVENDER
Lavandula dentata

FRENCH LAVENDER
Lavandula stoechas

LAVANDULA

L. angustifolia, also called *L. officinalis*, *L. spica*, *L. vera* (English lavender, true lavender); *L. dentata* (fringed lavender); *L. stoechas* (French lavender)

The long-lasting fragrant leaves and blossoms of lavender have been used for centuries in dried sachets, scented soaps, perfumes and aromatic tobaccos. Lavender salts have long been used as a stimulant to prevent fainting. In the garden, lavender makes a sweet-smelling border plant along paths or among rocks or as an edging to a herb garden.

All of the lavenders are bushy evergreens growing 30 to 90 cm (1 to 3 ft) tall, and all bear spikes of 6 to 12 mm ($\frac{1}{4}$ to $\frac{1}{2}$ in.) flowers, usually arranged in multiple whorls of six to 10 blossoms around each stem. Both the flowers and the foliage of all three plants have a sweet aroma, but the colours and configurations are somewhat different. Fringed lavender's 2.5 to 4 cm (1 to $1\frac{1}{2}$ in.), dark green foliage is fern-like, with deeply indented edges. French lavender and English lavender have 1.2 to 5 cm ($\frac{1}{2}$ to 2 in.) long, needle-like foliage but English lavender's leaves are blue-green while those of French lavender have a grey cast. Lavenders bloom from midsummer onwards; the English lavender bears grey-blue flowers, the fringed lavender bears blue flowers and the French lavender bears deep purple or white flowers.

HOW TO GROW. English lavender is hardy in all parts of Europe although it requires a mulch in cold and exposed northern parts to protect it from winter cold. The more delicate French lavender is native to the Mediterranean, but fully hardy even as far north as Britain. Fringed lavender is hardy only in southern Europe and must be taken indoors for the winter wherever temperatures are likely to fall below freezing. All lavenders flourish in direct sunlight and dry, sandy, well-drained, alkaline soil; infertile soil seems to improve the fragrance.

Because lavender seeds take about six weeks to germinate and the seedlings tend to grow very slowly, the plants are usually propagated from stem cuttings, which can be taken at any time of year. Plant rooted cuttings in the garden in the spring, in soil supplemented with ground limestone to neutralize any acidity. Space plants 60 to 90 cm (2 to 3 ft) apart. In the first year of growth, nip off the flower spikes before they bloom in order to make the bushes more compact. After flowering, cut all established plants lightly back; in order to prevent them from growing straggly, cut them back almost to ground level in early spring.

Harvest lavender flowers after the plant's second year; pick the leaves at any time. To harvest flowers, cut the stems just as buds start to open, when their colour and fragrance are greatest. Hang them in bunches, upside down, or dry them flat on a tray in a warm, airy, shady place for several weeks until they become crisp. Strip off the dried leaves and flowers from the stems and store them in an airtight container.

Fringed lavender can be grown indoors as a pot plant. It requires a minimum of five hours of direct sunlight a day. Use a proprietary potting compost supplemented with ground limestone. Feed with any house-plant fertilizer, diluted to half the recommended strength and used half as often as the packet suggests. Water until the soil is barely moist, and let the soil become dry between waterings. Indoor-grown lavender needs good air circulation around it to keep the leaves from blackening. As a pot plant, lavender usually grows only 30 to 60 cm (1 to 2 ft).

LEONTODON See *Taraxacum*

LEPIDIUM

L. sativum (garden cress, pepper cress)

Garden cress, an annual that grows 45 cm (1½ ft) tall, bears leaves that can be used as a salad ingredient. But most often garden cress is harvested for eating soon after germination, before the first true leaves develop. Then it is used as a peppery garnish for soups and sandwiches in combination with the similar seed leaves of mustard (*Sinapis alba*).

HOW TO GROW. Garden cress flourishes outdoors in all parts of Europe, in sun or light shade and a fertile, well-drained soil; seeds can be sown in the garden at intervals from very early spring through the summer to provide young leaves. At any time of the year, sow seeds thickly and evenly in shallow pots or other containers filled with potting compost or pads of moist cotton wool. Press the soil flat and water it, then place pots in bright light at a temperature of 18° to 21°C (65° to 70°F). In 10 to 12 days, seedlings will be ready for harvesting with scissors. If you grow mustard and cress together in the same container, sow the cress seed first and the mustard four days later, because mustard germinates more quickly.

LEVISTICUM

L. officinale, also called *Ligusticum paludapifolium* (lovage)

Lovage is a giant among herbs, a kitchen-garden plant that at maturity reaches a height of 0.9 to 2.1 metres (3 to 7 ft). It acquires this size over a period of about four years, dying back to the ground each winter. It is a perennial that somewhat resembles celery in appearance, taste and use. The dark green leaves are used as a salad green or to flavour soups and stews; the seeds add a celery and lemon-like flavour to many dishes, particularly cheese; the stems are sometimes candied like those of angelica; the roots can be cooked like a vegetable.

Lovage blooms in midsummer, producing umbrella-shaped clusters of small, yellowish-green flowers, 7.5 cm (3 in.) across, which are allowed to ripen for their seeds. Lovage does not mature until its second year, at which point a single plant will be ample for the needs of the average family.

HOW TO GROW. Lovage, native to southern Europe, thrives in all regions, though it does better in areas with cool weather to complete its growth cycle. It adapts to full sun or partial shade, and does best in a rich, moist soil, pH 6.0 to 7.0, supplemented with garden compost or manure. It can be started from seeds or root divisions; for best results the seeds must be sown as soon as they are ripe, but in any case must be less than three years old to germinate. Sow seeds outdoors in early autumn, covering them with about 6 mm (¼ in.) of soil, or sow seeds indoors in 7.5 to 10 cm (3 to 4 in.) peat pots in early spring. When night temperatures remain above 4°C (40°F) in the spring, set the plants out in the garden, placing them about 90 cm (3 ft) apart. You can also start lovage from root divisions in the spring. Fertilize every spring with a handful of general fertilizer hoed in around the base of each plant.

If lovage is grown for its leaves, do not let it flower. Leaves can generally be cut three times during the season: cut only the outside leaves, not the tender heart. To preserve leaves for winter use, dry them on their stems by hanging them in a cool, dark place; store in an airtight container. Seed heads intended for flavouring should be dried flat under the same conditions of light and temperature as for drying leaves, and stored in the same manner.

LIGUSTICUM See *Levisticum*

GARDEN CRESS
Lepidium sativum

LOVAGE
Levisticum officinale

LEMON VERBENA
Lippia citriodora

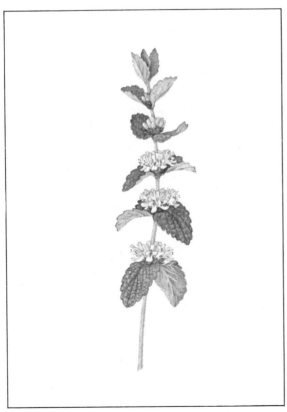

HOREHOUND
Marrubium vulgare

LIPPIA
L. citriodora, also called *Aloysia triphylla*, *L. triphylla* and
Verbena triphylla (lemon verbena)

Lemon verbena is an aromatic, semi-evergreen shrub whose lemon-scented leaves are used to flavour sweet dishes, fruit drinks, salads and iced soft beverages, and to perfume colognes, soaps and potpourri. Usually grown in tubs, this plant can be pruned to any height, although in its native Chile it grows 1.8 to 3 metres (6 to 10 ft) tall. When grown outdoors in frost-free regions, the narrow 5 to 10 cm (2 to 4 in.) leaves fall off during the winter and the plant appears dead until new growth appears the following spring. Tiny, barely perceptible mauve and white flowers bloom infrequently on slender panicles during the summer and autumn.

HOW TO GROW. Lemon verbena is not fully hardy and seldom survives severe winters in cold northern regions. In Britain, it usually withstands the average winter if planted in a warm and sheltered spot. Plant in any light, well-drained soil in full sun, spacing shrubs about 60 cm (2 ft) apart. In frost-prone regions, plant lemon verbena in pots to be placed outdoors in summer and brought indoors in winter before the first frost. Pot-grown plants thrive in a mixture of equal parts of loam, sand and leaf-mould, and do best with night temperatures of 10° to 13°C (50° to 55°F), rising to 21° to 24°C (70° to 75°F) in the daytime. They require at least five or six hours of direct sunlight a day. To promote new growth, cut back the stems of potted plants in February to within 15 cm (6 in.) of the soil, and for the same reason repot plants in a fresh soil mixture every two or three years. It is even better to discard old plants after two years, replacing them with young ones. To propagate, root stem cuttings of new growth taken in the spring. Lemon verbena is vulnerable to red spiders, and plants should be sprayed frequently and forcefully with plain water to control these pests.

To harvest lemon verbena, pick the leaves at any time and dry them rapidly in a warm, dark place. Stored in an airtight container, they will retain their fragrance for about two years.

M

MAJORANA See *Origanum*

MARRUBIUM
M. vulgare (horehound)

Musky, rather bitter-tasting horehound—taken in the form of syrup, boiled sweets, tea and even snuff—was once the sovereign remedy for coughs. It is a hardy perennial, 60 to 90 cm (2 to 3 ft) high, with velvety, aromatic leaves 2.5 to 5 cm (1 to 2 in.) long, and down-covered stems. From July to the end of September, tiny, white blossoms encircle the stems at intervals, providing bees with nectar for a tasty honey. The flowers are followed by seeds which, because they have hook-like appendages that fasten on to animals, often spread far afield, causing horehound to be regarded in some places as a weed.

HOW TO GROW. Horehound grows throughout Europe. It needs full sun but grows easily in any poor, dry soil, especially one that is chalky. Horehound may be started from seed sown in the spring or autumn; cover the seeds with 12 mm (½ in.) of soil. Horehound seedlings germinate erratically, and one may appear long before others. When the seedlings are 10 to 12.5 cm (4 to 5 in.) high, thin them to stand 20 to 25 cm (8 to 10 in.) apart; this relatively close spacing will help to keep the stems erect. Horehound needs little care except weeding.

MATRICARIA

M. chamomilla, also called *Chamomilla recutira* (German chamomile, scented mayweed)

German chamomile is often confused with sweet chamomile (see *Anthemis*). Both are used for herbal teas, but, although they share a common name, an apple-like fragrance and daisy-like flowers, the two plants are not botanically related. German chamomile grows 15 to 45 cm (6 to 18 in.) high, erect rather than creeping, and is an annual rather than a perennial. The yellow centres of its 2 cm ($\frac{3}{4}$ in.), white flowers are domed and hollow on the inside, and bloom at the ends of slender stems from spring to autumn. The deeply cut, shiny green leaves give the plant a feathery appearance.

HOW TO GROW. German chamomile can be grown in all parts of Europe. It needs full sun and will grow in any light, dry soil. Sow seeds in late summer or early spring, or start them indoors in seed trays or pots in late winter. Sprinkle them on top of the soil; do not cover—they are very fine—and keep the soil moist but not soggy during the germination period. Thin or transplant the seedlings to stand 20 to 30 cm (8 to 12 in.) apart.

Harvest German chamomile when the flowers are in full bloom and on a sunny day. Spread the flower heads thinly on a clean cloth and dry them in the sun. Then remove and discard any leaves or pieces of stem; store the flowers in an airtight container in a cool, dry place.

MATRICARIA EXIMIA See *Chrysanthemum*

MELISSA

M. officinalis (lemon balm, balm, sweet balm)

Often confused with lemon thyme and lemon verbena, lemon balm is a mint-like, fast-spreading perennial 60 to 90 cm (2 to 3 ft) tall and equally wide, grown for its lemon-scented leaves, which are used as a seasoning for egg dishes, veal or poultry, floated on cold drinks, brewed in teas and used in the manufacture of liqueurs and cordials. Lemon balm's leaves are 2.5 to 7.5 cm (1 to 3 in.) long, and from early summer into autumn the plant produces small clusters of inconspicuous, creamy-white flowers which are rich in nectar.

HOW TO GROW. Lemon balm is native to southern Europe and has been cultivated for thousands of years. It grows throughout Europe and does best in full sun or light shade and a light, dry, relatively poor soil with a pH of 6.0 to 8.0. Like other lemon-scented herbs, it produces more intense flavour and aroma under poor growing conditions. Seeds germinate slowly and should be sown indoors in late winter or early spring for transplanting outdoors when all danger of frost is past; or, better still, sow seeds outdoors in late autumn to germinate the following spring. Do not cover the seeds with soil; they are very tiny. When seedlings are about 5 cm (2 in.) high, thin or transplant them to stand 45 cm ($1\frac{1}{2}$ ft) apart. It is easier to start plants from root divisions in early spring, when the new leaves first appear, or from stem cuttings taken in spring or summer.

Fresh leaves of lemon balm can be picked for use at any time. To harvest leaves for drying, cut just before flowering and spread on a tray or screen in the shade. To retain colour and flavour, dry the leaves as quickly as possible, preferably in a cool oven. Store them in an airtight container. Lemon balm is not of great culinary importance, but the dried leaves add a pleasant lemon aroma to linen sachets and potpourris.

Lemon balm grown indoors requires at least five hours of direct sunlight a day or 14 to 16 hours of artificial light.

GERMAN CHAMOMILE
Matricaria chamomilla

LEMON BALM
Melissa officinalis

PEPPERMINT
Mentha x *piperita*

PENNYROYAL
Mentha pulegium

Start plants from seed at any time, or bring plants in from the garden in late summer. Lemon balm grown indoors should be pruned periodically to produce a bushy plant 15 to 20 cm (6 to 8 in.) high; leaves for flavouring can be picked when the plant reaches a height of 15 cm (6 in.).

MENTHA

M. x *piperita* (peppermint); *M. pulegium* (pennyroyal); *M. rotundifolia* (apple mint, round-leaved mint, woolly mint); *M. spicata* (spearmint, common mint)

The mints are a large and popular family of herbs, cultivated for their intensely flavoured, cool-tasting leaves. They grow easily and spread rapidly through wandering, deep-reaching roots which, if not contained, quickly invade parts of the garden where they are not wanted. The mints listed here are perennials. Their stems are between 30 to 90 cm (1 to 3 ft) tall and bear pairs of opposite, tooth-edged leaves; their tiny flowers bloom in clusters in terminal spikes and are usually followed by round, brown seeds.

Peppermint can be identified by its fragrant leaves, which grow on short stalks. The varieties in cultivation are usually known as black peppermint (*M.* x *piperita* var. *piperita*), with dark-coloured stems, and white peppermint (*M.* x *piperita pallescens*), with white stems. Its dense spikes of violet flowers bloom in late summer, but since peppermint comes from crosses with other mints, it is sterile and the flowers rarely go to seed. Consequently, it can be propagated only by stem cuttings or root divisions. It is rarely used in cooking, but the oil extracted from the leaves is used commercially to flavour sweets as well as several liqueurs, in particular crème de menthe.

Pennyroyal, a bitter-tasting mint whose unusual flavour is no longer popular, makes an aromatic ground cover. In former times, it was used as a medicinal herb for coughs and as an insect repellent (the Latin name *pulegium* comes from *pulex*, Latin for flea). The plant's creeping stems, 45 to 60 cm (1½ to 2 ft) long, have oval leaves covered with tiny hairs. In midsummer, lavender-blue or pink flowers rise in tiers on 15 to 30 cm (6 to 12 in.) flower spikes above the otherwise prostrate plant.

Apple mint is sometimes called round-leaved mint; its 2.5 to 10 cm (1 to 4 in.) rounded leaves have wrinkled surfaces which are covered with a dense whitish down. This fruity-tasting mint grows 15 to 90 cm (6 in. to 3 ft) tall and in midsummer bears 5 to 10 cm (2 to 4 in.), branching spikes of greyish-white blossoms that deepen to pink or violet. Apple mint is considered the finest mint for culinary purposes, particularly the cultivar 'Bowles' Variety'. For decorative purposes in fresh flower arrangements, the cultivar 'Variegata', pineapple mint, has foliage streaked with pale yellow or white and grows only 25 cm (10 in.) tall.

Spearmint, the classic ingredient in mint juleps, is the most strongly flavoured of the mints. Its leaves can be floated in drinks, used for sauces and jellies, cooked with young vegetables, especially new potatoes, carrots and peas or eaten fresh in salads. Its erect stems grow 30 to 60 cm (1 to 2 ft) tall, and its leaves, practically hairless and deeply veined, are about 5 cm (2 in.) long. In midsummer, dense flower spikes of violet or pink blossoms rise above the green foliage on a central stem.

HOW TO GROW. All the mints except pennyroyal are hardy throughout Europe, being for the most part native to the Mediterranean region. Pennyroyal is not hardy where winter temperatures fall below −15°C (5°F) and needs to be moved indoors. The mints grow well in both direct sunlight or partial shade and do best in rich, fairly moist soil with a pH of 5.5 to 6.5, supplemented with garden compost.

Apple mint will also grow in soil with less moisture.

To prevent mint from taking over the garden, choose a restricted position, or block the wandering roots with underground barriers of roof tiles 15 to 25 cm (6 to 10 in.) deep. Mint can also be planted in flower pots or open-ended buckets sunk into the earth. Dig garden compost into the soil to enrich it, but do not use manure; the latter carries a disfiguring mint rust fungus. Mints are usually started in the spring or autumn from root divisions, set 30 to 38 cm (1 to 1¼ ft) apart, or from stem cuttings. To increase the plant's production, nip off flower spikes before they open. Where winter temperatures remain below −18°C (0°F) for extended periods, protect plants with a mulch of bracken or straw. Each spring, chop matted mint roots with a sharp spade 7.5 to 10 cm (3 to 4 in.) deep. Sprinkle garden compost or a dusting of a general fertilizer over the ground at this time. Renew mints every three years by dividing and replanting the roots in the spring or autumn. At this time peppermint, which does not do well in the same place for more than a few years, should be transferred to a new site.

Mint leaves can be picked for use fresh at any time. To harvest the leaves for drying, cut the stems down to the first two sets of leaves just before the flowers open. Hang upside down to dry in a warm, dark, well-ventilated place. Pick the dried leaves from the stems and rub them between the palms of the hands to crush them slightly; then store them in an airtight container. Dried mint quickly loses its flavour and the leaves are better frozen; or better still, dig up one or two roots in autumn and plant them in deep pots. If kept at a temperature of about 13°C (55°F), fresh leaves can be harvested during the winter.

All mints can be grown indoors, but apple mint makes the most handsome, compact plant; the other species tend to sprawl. Indoor mints require at least five hours of strong, direct sunlight a day. Pot in the spring in containers that provide room for the creeping roots. Use a proprietary potting compost. Cut back stems frequently to 10 to 15 cm (4 to 6 in.) for better-tasting leaves and to stop the plants from flowering. Keep the soil moist but not soggy, and feed with a liquid house-plant fertilizer, used at half the recommended strength, every three to four weeks. If plants start to yellow, repot them in a larger container or divide the mass of roots into small sections and repot into separate pots.

MONARDA
M. didyma (bergamot, bee balm, Oswego tea)

Bergamot is a striking member of the mint family that stands 90 cm (3 ft) tall on an erect stem and produces shaggy, flaming-red flowers, 5 to 7.5 cm (2 to 3 in.) across, made up of numerous trumpet-shaped florets. These aromatic flowers bloom throughout the summer and are a great favourite with bees. They make fine cut flowers. Bergamot is native to the United States and its citrus-flavoured leaves, 10 to 15 cm (4 to 6 in.) long, were used as a tea by the Oswego Indians. Oswego tea was also drunk by the rebellious colonial patriots who were boycotting British tea at the time of the Boston Tea Party. Today, bergamot leaves are most often used as flavouring for fruit cups and preserves. Commercially it is used in the perfume industry.

HOW TO GROW. Bergamot grows in temperate and mild parts of Europe. It does best in full sun but tolerates light shade, and will thrive in any moist soil that is rich in organic matter such as manure, garden compost or leaf-mould. When grown from seed, it takes more than a year to become established, so it is usually started from nursery stock or root divisions. The latter are easy to take,

APPLE MINT
Mentha rotundifolia

SPEARMINT
Mentha spicata

BERGAMOT
Monarda didyma

SWEET CICELY
Myrrhis odorata

MYRTLE
Myrtus communis

for bergamot's roots are shallow and far ranging. Dig up the root clump in the early spring, discard the inner older portion, and set the divisions 30 to 38 cm (1 to 1¼ ft) apart. To increase the strength of seedling-grown plants in later years, cut off the flower heads before they bloom the first year. Thereafter, cutting flowers right after they bloom often stimulates a second flowering in the same year. Weed bergamot by hand to avoid damaging the shallow roots. In the autumn, cut the plants down to within 2.5 cm (1 in.) of the ground. Every three or four years, bergamot clumps should be divided to prevent overcrowding.

Bergamot leaves can be harvested just before the plant flowers. To dry the leaves, strip them from the stalk and dry in the shade on a screen or tray for two or three days, then store in an airtight container.

MYRRHIS
M. odorata (sweet cicely, giant chervil, anise fern)

Sweet cicely, described as "that herbe of very good and pleasant smell" by the 16th-century English herbalist Gerard, is a graceful 60 to 90 cm (2 to 3 ft) high perennial whose every part—seeds, roots, leaves and blossoms—is pervaded by a sweet, anise-like taste and fragrance. The taproot can be cooked and eaten as a vegetable, and the oil extracted from its seeds is used commercially as a flavouring in liqueurs, but it is grown in gardens mainly for its handsome, lacy foliage, which is downy on the underside. In the late spring, the plant's tall, hollow stems bear 4 to 10 cm (2 to 4 in.) clusters of white flowers which are attractive to bees; the flowers are followed by crowns of shiny, brownish-black seeds 2 to 2.5 cm (¾ to 1 in.) long.

HOW TO GROW. Sweet cicely grows wild in northern Europe, but does not flower in hot climates. It needs partial shade and a moist, acid soil of pH 5.5 to 6.5, supplemented with garden compost or manure. Dig the bed deep, to accommodate the plant's deep taproot, and sow the seeds in the late summer or early autumn covering them with 6 mm (¼ in.) of soil; sweet cicely seeds germinate best after freezing during the winter months. In the spring, when the seedlings are about 5 cm (2 in.) tall, thin them to stand 60 cm (2 ft) apart. If seeds are allowed to dry and fall from the plant, sweet cicely will seed itself. It can also be propagated from upper sections of the taproot; make sure, however, that each section contains an eye.

Leaves can be harvested for use fresh from the time they unfold in spring until late autumn. Seeds may be harvested when they are ripe, but many gardeners prefer to pick green, immature seeds in midsummer to flavour herb mixtures and salads. The dried leaves can also be added to potpourris.

MYRTUS
M. communis (myrtle)

One of several plants used by the ancient Greeks to make crowns for poets and athletes, this species of myrtle is a dense evergreen shrub hardy only in warm regions. Under ideal conditions it grows to a height of 3 to 5 metres (10 to 15 ft), but most garden plants grow 1 to 2.4 metres (3 to 8 ft) tall, depending on the variety. Plants grown in pots are usually about 60 cm (2 ft) high. Every part of the myrtle—leaves, flowers, berries and bark—is aromatic. In the mountain districts of southern Europe, myrtle is a popular flavouring for meat: large sprigs are added to open fires to flavour roast lamb and kid, and small, roasted game birds are often stuffed with or wrapped in fresh leaves.

The shiny leaves, 2.5 to 5 cm (1 to 2 in.) long, give off a particularly strong and pleasant scent when crushed. The sweet-smelling, white flowers, 2 cm (¾ in.) across, bloom from late spring to midsummer. They are followed by 12 mm (½ in.) berries, which the Athenians dried and used as a condiment, like pepper. Myrtle also provides an excellent hedge.

HOW TO GROW. Myrtle grows outdoors all year only in southern regions of Europe. In mild regions it may be grown as a wall shrub in a sheltered position, but elsewhere it is best grown in pots or tubs and moved indoors during the winter. It will grow in sun or light shade in almost any well-drained garden soil, but it does not tolerate wet soil. Myrtle is easily propagated from cuttings of half-ripened shoots taken in midsummer; it can also be grown from seeds or by layering.

When it is grown as a hedge in frost-free regions, myrtle should be pruned in the spring, before new growth starts. It can be trained to any desired shape and size. Myrtle grown indoors tolerates low light conditions; even reflected light near a window is adequate.

N

NASTURTIUM
N. officinale, also called *Rorippa nasturtium-aquaticum* (watercress)

Peppery-tasting watercress is a semi-aquatic, creeping perennial whose leaves are popular in salads, soups and as a garnish for sandwiches and meat dishes; it should not be confused with *Tropaeolum majus*, which is commonly called nasturtium. The many-branched plant grows in shallow water, either submerged or floating, its stems stretching 60 cm (2 ft) or more in length. Each dark green compound leaf consists of three to 11 leaflets, 1.2 to 2 cm (½ to ¾ in.) across, growing off a slightly paler stem that is usually submerged; each group of leaflets is between 12.5 to 15 cm (5 to 6 in.) long. Watercress keeps sending out new roots and a single plant will grow indefinitely until freezing weather. During the early summer, small, white, four-petalled flowers bloom in loose clusters at the extreme ends of the stems. These should be removed to encourage the production of leaves. Watercress is available as dark green or bronzy cultivars; the latter are easier to grow and have more flavour.

HOW TO GROW. Watercress can be grown throughout Europe in gardens, and it is also cultivated on a large commercial scale. It grows best in shallow, slowly moving water, particularly cool streams, although it can also be grown in improvised irrigation trenches or even boxes filled with very rich garden soil, kept permanently moist and set away from direct sunshine. Plants can be raised from seed or stem cuttings—fresh sprigs from a greengrocer's are easy to root. Scatter seeds or set plants against the muddy banks of a watercourse; they will grow without further attention and can be harvested as desired.

NEPETA
N. cataria (catmint, catnip)

Catmint is noted for the way its leaves and blossoms delight cats of all sizes, from the wild mountain lion to the domestic tabby. This catmint ecstasy seems to affect only felines, but the lemony-mint-scented leaves have also been used by humans for brewing tea and in former days were used to flavour meats and salads. The hardy perennial grows 60 to 90 cm (2 to 3 ft) tall and has 5 to 7.5 cm (2 to 3 in.) long, heart-shaped, grey-green leaves, with downy grey undersides. They are arranged in pairs on thick, strong stems that are capped from midsummer to late summer with flower spikes densely covered with small, pale pink or

WATERCRESS
Nasturtium officinale

CATMINT
Nepeta cataria

white blossoms. The flower spikes attract bees.

HOW TO GROW. Catmint grows in most parts of Europe; it is rare as a wild plant in Britain. It grows in any soil but prefers a moist, rich site. It thrives in partial shade, tolerates sun and can be grown from seed sown in autumn or spring, although autumn sowing germinates best. Sow the seeds where the plants are to grow; when seedlings are 5 to 7.5 cm (2 to 3 in.) tall, thin them to stand 30 to 45 cm (1 to 1½ ft) apart. Plants can also be started from root divisions in the spring. Except for weeding, catmint requires little care.

If you pinch back the plant when the first flower buds form, it will become bushy enough to produce as many as three successive harvests of leaves. To harvest, cut off the top leaves and flowers and dry them for two or three days in a shady place, then strip the leaves and flowers from the stems and store in an airtight container. Catmint seeds remain viable for four or five years.

Catmint grown indoors as a house plant needs moist but not soggy soil and at least five hours of direct sunlight a day. It does best in temperatures of 13° to 15°C (55° to 60°F). Start indoor plants from seed, using a 10 cm (4 in.) pot filled with a proprietary seed compost. Prune to preserve a bushy shape; catmint grown indoors tends to become straggly.

O

OCIMUM
O. basilicum (sweet basil)

Sweet basil, a native of tropical Pacific islands, is a bushy annual, 38 to 60 cm (1¾ to 2 ft) high, whose aromatic leaves exude a pleasant clove-like fragrance even when lightly brushed. A popular flavouring for tomatoes, it is used in quantity for a green sauce—called *pesto* in Italy and *pistou* in France—that is added to soups, vegetables, fish and pasta in Mediterranean cookery. Several ornamental cultivars, grown mainly for their colourful foliage, are available.

The silky leaves of sweet basil grow 2.5 to 5 cm (1 to 2 in.) long. From midsummer on, whorls of 3 to 6 mm (⅛ to ¼ in.), white blossoms form on spikes at the ends of the stems. The leaves can be harvested continuously throughout the growing season, and are at their most delicious when quite young.

HOW TO GROW. Sweet basil is an easily grown, warm-climate plant, sensitive to frost, that requires full sun and a well-drained soil with a pH of 5.5 to 6.5 supplemented with manure or garden compost. It thrives in Mediterranean climates. In cooler regions sow seeds under glass in early spring. Transplant seedlings to individual pots when 2.5 cm (1 in.) tall. Basil transplants readily and grows rapidly if temperatures are 21°C (70°F) or above. Transfer seedlings to the garden when all danger of frost is past. Or sow seeds outdoors when the danger of frost is past, covering them with 6 mm (¼ in.) of soil. When the seedlings are 5 to 7.5 cm (2 to 3 in.) tall, thin or transplant them to stand 30 cm (1 ft) apart. Pinch off the tops when the plants are 12.5 to 15 cm (5 to 6 in.) high to encourage bushy growth. Harvest fresh leaves at any time, cutting plants to within 15 cm (6 in.) of the ground if desired. The best flavour, however, comes from young plants, and for a continuous supply during summer it is advisable to make successive sowings at fortnightly intervals.

To harvest basil for drying, cut the stems just before the flowers open, strip the leaves from the stems and dry them on trays in a dark, airy place. When the leaves are dry, store them in an airtight container. Dried basil tends to lose its flavour quickly and is better frozen or preserved, Italian style, between layers of salt in a jar and topped with

SWEET BASIL
Ocimum basilicum

olive oil. In a refrigerator, the leaves will keep their flavour for several months, though they tend to go black.

Basil can also be grown indoors as a pot plant; ornamental cultivars are particularly suited to this purpose, being both decorative and useful. Both types need at least five hours of direct sunlight daily or 12 hours of artificial light, and require a barely moist soil. Garden seedlings no more than 15 cm (6 in.) tall can be put into 15 cm (6 in.) pots filled with potting compost and moved indoors to a sunny window sill. Or seeds can be sown in pots at any time of year. Feed indoor plants about once a month with an all-purpose liquid fertilizer, used at half strength.

ORIGANUM
O. dictamnus, more usually called *Amaracus dictamnus* (dittany of Crete, hop marjoram); *O. majorana* more usually called *Majorana hortensis* (sweet marjoram, knotted marjoram); *O. onites* (pot marjoram); *O. vulgare* (oregano, wild marjoram)

The different *Origanum* species have long baffled herbalists and gardeners because their seeds look alike and so do the plants in their early stages of growth. Dittany when young is identical in appearance to oregano, for instance, except for the larger size of its leaves. It also smells like oregano, yet it lacks that plant's pungent taste. But unlike oregano, dittany is grown chiefly for decoration, although its leaves can be eaten in salads or used for herbal teas. In the same way, mild-flavoured sweet marjoram, pot marjoram and strong-flavoured oregano are often mistakenly sold for each other because the plants resemble each other so closely. All three are cooking herbs. Sweet and pot marjoram are among the most popular herbs in European cooking; they have a flavour reminiscent of thyme though sweeter, especially in sweet marjoram. The leaves, which lose their flavour if cooked for a long time, are used to season many types of savoury dishes, including meat, poultry, stews and stuffings, egg dishes and soups. The finely chopped leaves are also good in salad dressings. Oregano has a more pungent flavour than the marjorams; it is a traditional ingredient in Italian pizzas and is used to flavour tomato, cheese, fish and vegetable dishes. Oregano's flavour is most pronounced when grown in hot, sunny climates; the dried variety commonly sold, neither tastes nor smells like the Italian oregano, and is botanically unrelated to oregano.

Dittany is a tender perennial, about 30 cm (1 ft) tall, that produces drooping heads of tiny, purplish-pink flowers during the late summer. Sweet marjoram is a tender perennial, 20 to 25 cm (8 to 10 in.) high, usually grown as a half-hardy annual except in the mild climate of the Mediterranean; it produces very inconspicuous, pinkish-white blossoms 10 or 12 weeks after seeds are sown. Pot marjoram is hardy and can be grown as a perennial. It reaches a height of 30 cm (1 ft) and bears white flowers; the leaves are more bitter than those of sweet marjoram. Oregano, a hardy perennial, grows 60 to 75 cm (2 to 2½ ft) tall and produces 7.5 to 10 cm (3 to 4 in.) clusters of small, purplish-pink flowers in summer and autumn.

HOW TO GROW. Sweet marjoram and oregano can be grown outdoors in temperate and southern Europe, but in northern regions pot marjoram is often preferred as it is fully hardy, though with more bitter-tasting leaves. Dittany is usually grown in pots or hanging baskets kept outdoors in the summer and brought indoors wherever winter temperatures fall below 7°C (45°F). All four kinds of origanum need full sun and do best in light, dry, well-drained soil with a pH between 6.0 and 8.0.

DITTANY OF CRETE
Origanum dictamnus

SWEET MARJORAM
Origanum majorana

OREGANO
Origanum vulgare

SWEET OLIVE
Osmanthus fragrans

LEMON-SCENTED GERANIUM
Pelargonium x *citrosum*

Dittany can be propagated from stem cuttings taken in the spring and rooted in moist sand. Pot rooted cuttings in a proprietary potting compost. Give the plants direct sunlight; water them well; then allow to dry out between waterings. When night temperatures remain above 7°C (45°F) move them outdoors. In autumn, cut off the flowering stems and transfer plants indoors for the winter. Water only enough to prevent wilting during the winter months. Dittany can also be grown indoors all year round; for this it requires at least five hours of direct sunlight a day. Indoors, flower buds have to be pinched off to stimulate leaf growth; the plant may flower and die if this is not done.

Sweet and pot marjoram and oregano can be raised from seed. The seeds germinate best if they are sown indoors in trays or pots or in cold frames in early spring for transfer outdoors when temperatures remain above 7°C (45°F). They can also be sown directly in the garden when temperatures remain above 7°C (45°F). Cover the seeds with no more than 2 mm ($\frac{1}{16}$ in.) of soil. They usually germinate in eight to 10 days. When plants are 5 to 7.5 cm (2 to 3 in.) high, thin or transplant them to stand 20 to 38 cm (8 to 15 in.) apart. During the early stages of development, control weeds by cultivating round the base of plants and water only if leaves begin to wilt. When the plants are 15 cm (6 in.) high, pinch back the tips to encourage branching and bushy growth. Sweet marjoram can also be propagated from stem cuttings and oregano can be propagated by dividing roots in spring or autumn. In fact, the tangled roots of oregano should be divided every two or three years, since older plants have less flavour. Marjorams also increase by self-seeding.

Leaves and stem tips of sweet and pot marjoram and oregano can be cut for use as soon as the plants are 10 to 12.5 cm (4 to 5 in.) high, but their flavour is best after the flower buds form. To harvest, cut the stem tops down to the first two sets of leaves. New stems and shoots will grow, producing second and sometimes third crops. Dry the leaves in a warm, dry, shaded place, and store them in an airtight container. Sweet and pot marjoram are also suitable for freezing; oregano is nearly always sold dried which improves its flavour.

Sweet marjoram can be grown in pots indoors. Start from either seeds or plants, and treat exactly like dittany. Pinch back stem tips to encourage bushy growth, and feed plants with a liquid general fertilizer diluted to half the recommended strength at monthly intervals.

OSMANTHUS
O. fragrans (sweet olive)

Sweet olive is an evergreen shrub with flowers that give off a strong, pleasant, orange-like aroma. It is a native of Asia, where it grows to a height of 9 metres (30 ft), but in cultivation it seldom reaches a height of more than 3 metres (10 ft). Its 6 mm ($\frac{1}{4}$ in.) flowers, so tiny they are hard to see, bloom profusely in late winter and spring and may appear intermittently at other seasons. The 6 to 10 cm ($2\frac{1}{2}$ to 4 in.) long leaves are dark green, holly-like and leathery, with smooth or finely serrated edges.

HOW TO GROW. Sweet olive is hardy only in frost-free regions; it does best where it is shaded from the midday sun and protected from wind. It will grow in almost any well-drained soil, kept barely moist, that contains about one-third organic material such as moss peat or leaf-mould. Propagate plants from cuttings taken in late summer. Sweet olive can be grown indoors for its fragrance but grows very slowly; even old plants rarely exceed a height of 60 to 90 cm (2 to 3 ft). Do not allow the soil to dry out; it should be kept slightly moist. Feed indoor plants monthly with a house-plant fertilizer diluted to half the recommended strength, and give them bright reflected or indirect light.

P

PELARGONIUM

P. x *citrosum*, also called *P. crispum* (lemon-scented geranium); *P.* x *domesticum* 'Clorinda' (Clorinda geranium); *P. graveolens* (rose-scented geranium); *P. tomentosum* (peppermint-scented geranium)

Geraniums, correctly called pelargoniums, include many scented species and cultivars whose leaves are used as herbs for flavouring and scenting beverages, preserves, desserts and other foods and, especially in combination, as ingredients for fragrant potpourri. Commercially they are grown for the perfume industry—the rose-scented geranium oil from the Island of Réunion is a well-known example. The scents are carried by the leaves, which release aromatic oils when touched or, in some cases, in strong, hot sun. Like other geraniums, the ones with scented leaves are tender, shrubby plants, mainly native to southern Africa but now grown throughout the world. Their flowers are generally unspectacular.

Lemon-scented geraniums are slender plants 60 to 90 cm (2 to 3 ft) tall that look like miniature trees. Their stiff, rough, three-lobed leaves are tiny—no larger than 2.5 cm (1 in.) across—and have curly serrated edges; they grow on 2.5 to 5 cm (1 to 2 in.) stems. Lavender flowers, up to 5 cm (2 in.) across, appear during the summer at the top of the plant, usually in clusters of two and three on 2.5 to 5 cm (1 to 2 in.) stems.

Clorinda geranium is one of the showiest of the scented geraniums, with large clusters of rose-pink flowers streaked with orange-red. It is a sturdy trailing plant; its three-lobed, rough-textured, dusty-green leaves smell like eucalyptus when bruised.

Rose-scented geraniums have hairy, upright stalks that may reach a height of 90 cm (3 ft). They are topped by umbrella-like clusters of five to 10 tiny flowers of deep rose or lavender with a red spot in the centre of each. The heart-shaped, deeply indented, grey-green leaves become as much as 10 cm (4 in.) wide and are borne intermittently throughout the summer on stems up to 7.5 cm (3 in.) long.

The peppermint-scented geranium is also a trailing plant; its velvety, heart-shaped leaves, often 10 cm (4 in.) wide, are emerald-green and appear on thick, soft, hairy stems up to 15 cm (6 in.) long. The few, tiny, white flowers bloom in summer, in clusters on stems that also grow as long as 15 cm (6 in.).

HOW TO GROW. Although the peppermint geranium tolerates light shade, all scented geraniums do best in full sun, in well-drained soil that is slightly on the dry side. They can be grown outdoors only in frost-free climates, and elsewhere are used for summer bedding; they must be potted and brought indoors in the winter. While scented geraniums can be raised from seed, the resulting plants may not bear the scent of the parent. To be sure of scented leaves, buy true-to-name cultivars from geranium specialists. Although all geraniums can be propagated from root cuttings, the universal propagation method is by stem cuttings, taken at any time; they root well in barely damp, coarse sand.

Grown indoors as house plants, scented geraniums need at least five hours of direct sunlight a day, or 14 to 18 hours of artificial light. When repotting becomes necessary, use a proprietary potting compost. Let the soil get barely dry before watering. If it is allowed to get very dry, the lower

CLORINDA GERANIUM
Pelargonium x *domesticum* 'Clorinda'

ROSE-SCENTED GERANIUM
Pelargonium graveolens

PEPPERMINT-SCENTED GERANIUM
Pelargonium tomentosum

PURPLE PERILLA
Perilla frutescens var. *crispa*

leaves will turn yellow and fall off. Feed with any house-plant fertilizer, used at half the recommended strength, every two weeks during the flowering season and monthly for the rest of the year.

PERILLA
P. frutescens var. *crispa*, also called *P. frutescens* 'Nankinensis' (purple perilla, summer coleus, beefsteak plant)

Purple perilla is often grown in herb gardens for its ornamental foliage that gives off a spicy, cinnamon-like fragrance when rubbed or bruised. In Japan the leaves, seeds and flower spikes are a basic culinary herb, *shisho*. The dark leaves with their deeply fringed edges resemble those of coleus, hence the common name summer coleus, but in fact the two plants are unrelated. Perilla is an erect annual, 60 cm (2 ft) or more tall, with branching, burgundy-coloured stems. The large leaves, 7.5 to 15 cm (3 to 6 in.) long, are covered on top with whitish hairs and underneath with purple ones. In summer, the plant produces short flower spikes bearing inconspicuous, pinkish-green blossoms. Most gardeners pinch out the flower spikes as they develop to encourage more of the colourful foliage on bushy plants. The cultivar 'Foliis Atropurpurea Laciniata' has even deeper purple leaves, deeply incised.

HOW TO GROW. Purple perilla is half-hardy in temperate Europe, fully hardy in the south. It will grow in any soil in full sun or partial shade. To achieve the earliest outdoor seedlings, sow the seeds in late winter or early spring and plant out in the open when all danger of frost is past. Thin or transplant seedlings to stand 23 to 30 cm (9 to 12 in.) apart. When plants are 15 cm (6 in.) tall, pinch off the tips to stimulate branching, and repeat pinching at each 15 cm (6 in.) increment of growth. Perilla will die with the first frost, but if some of the flower spikes are permitted to mature, the plant will seed itself and seedlings will appear the following spring in mild regions. Perillas can also be grown as indoor pot plants; pot them up in a proprietary potting compost when 10 cm (4 in.) high and keep in a well-lit place.

PETROSELINUM
P. crispum ssp. *crispum* (parsley); *P. crispum* ssp. *tuberosum* (Hamburg parsley)

Parsley is a hardy biennial, usually cultivated as an annual and much used in cooking and for garnishing. There are curly and plain-leaved types of parsley and some cooks contend that plain-leaved parsley has a stronger flavour and is superior for cooking, but this is probably due to soil and climate factors, plain-leaved parsley being hardier and tougher than the curly kind.

Parsley is the most commonly grown herb and is steeped in traditions and folklore. It was used by the ancient Greeks and Romans, chiefly as decoration, in the belief that parsley sprigs stimulated the appetite and *joie de vivre*. In the Middle Ages, parsley was surrounded by superstitions, and it was thought that transplanted seedlings were an invitation to death and general poor harvest (it still remains true that parsley seedlings do not transplant well). The English herbalist Culpeper warned his contemporaries against excessive use of parsley as it increased the sexual appetite; and in some country districts time-honoured traditions demanded that parsley be sown, preferably by moonlight, at midnight on Good Friday.

Parsley is indispensable for many culinary dishes: it is essential in a *bouquet garni* for stocks and stews, in a number of classic sauces, such as tartar sauce and parsley sauce, in *maître d'hôtel* butter and in salad dressings. It can be added to most meat, poultry, fish, shellfish and vegetable dishes. Small fresh sprigs or finely chopped leaves are universally used for garnish.

Parsley grows 25 to 30 cm (10 to 12 in.) tall in the first year. In the second year 60 cm (2 ft) tall flower stalks appear, and their blossoms ripen into brown seeds that will remain viable for a period of two to three years. Flowering stems should be removed to encourage leaf production.

Hamburg parsley, sometimes called turnip-rooted parsley, is grown as an annual vegetable for its long tap-roots which are cooked and eaten like parsnips. The leaves can be used for flavouring in the same way as curly or plain-leaved parsley, but they are coarser and lack the flavour of true parsley.

HOW TO GROW. Parsley grows in all parts of Europe. It thrives in full sun but will tolerate very light shade and needs rich, well-drained soil with a pH of 5.0 to 7.0, supplemented with manure or compost. In most areas, sow seeds outdoors in the early spring, and again in summer for a winter crop. Sow seeds 6 mm ($\frac{1}{4}$ in.) deep. Parsley seeds are extremely slow to germinate, sometimes taking eight to nine weeks. To speed germination in the spring, soak seeds in lukewarm water for 24 hours before sowing or water the drills with warm water. In areas where summer temperatures exceed 32°C (90°F) for pro-longed periods, sow seeds in the autumn. While the seeds are germinating, the bed should be watered as necessary to keep it from becoming dry. Thin seedlings to stand 7.5 cm (3 in.) apart when they are 5 to 7.5 cm (2 to 3 in.) high. Allow plants to spread until they touch, then pull and use every other plant. Continue harvesting alternate plants until they stand 30 cm (1 ft) apart. When plants reach a height of 10 cm (4 in.) feed them with a general fertilizer at the rate of 85 grams (3 oz) for every 3 metres (10 ft) of row. Repeat this feeding a month later.

Parsley leaves can be harvested as soon as the plant is 15 cm (6 in.) tall. Fresh leaves can be stored in the refrigerator for 24 hours or they can be frozen or even dried, although the latter method causes great loss of flavour. To dry the leaves, spread them out on a screen in a shady and well-ventilated place. Finally, store them in an airtight container.

Parsley can be grown indoors, in ordinary flower pots or in special, small-lipped parsley pots using any standard potting compost. It needs at least five hours of direct sunlight a day or 12 hours of strong artificial light, and does best in day temperatures below 21°C (70°F). To grow parsley from seed indoors, sprinkle half a dozen seeds on the top of a 10 to 15 cm (4 to 6 in.) pot filled with potting compost and moisten by setting the pot in lukewarm water. Place the pot in bright indirect light until seeds germinate. Once seedlings appear, transfer to full sun or strong light, on the kitchen window sill, for instance, and keep the soil moist but not soggy. Do not thin plants; grown close together the six plants per pot provide a steady supply of parsley for cutting. Outdoor garden plants can be potted in late summer and brought indoors to grow on a cool, sunny window sill, where they will produce fresh leaves for harvesting throughout winter.

To grow Hamburg parsley for a vegetable crop, sow the seeds outdoors in mid-spring, just covering them with soil. Choose a well-drained, fertile soil in full sun. When the seedlings are about 5 cm (2 in.) high, thin them to stand 25 cm (10 in.) apart. Harvest the roots from early autumn onwards; they can be lifted and stored in boxes of sand or be dug up and used as required.

PEUCEDANUM See *Anethum*

PARSLEY
Petroselinum crispum ssp. *crispum*

HAMBURG PARSLEY
Petroselinum crispum ssp. *tuberosum*

ANISE
Pimpinella anisum

Illustration by Mary Ann Hodson—The Garden Studio

PURSLANE
Portulaca oleracea

PIMPINELLA

P. anisum also called *Anisum vulgare* (anise, aniseed)

Sweet-tasting, sweet-smelling anise has been grown for centuries for its liquorice-flavoured and liquorice-scented seeds, which are used in cakes and confections, in toiletries and medicines and in liqueurs and cordials. Anise is grown in southern Europe on a vast commercial scale, chiefly to flavour alcoholic beverages collectively known as pastis which include Pernod, Ricard, ouzo and arrak; in India the seeds go into curry mixtures, and lightly roasted seeds are chewed as an aid to the digestion and to sweeten the breath.

This 45 to 60 cm (1½ to 2 ft) tall annual has two extremely different kinds of foliage: the basal leaves, about 2 cm (¾ in.) long, are bright green and pear-shaped with deeply notched edges; the leaves along the flower stalks are feathery and finely cut, and are sometimes used as a garnish. In midsummer, lacy, white blossoms form airy, umbrella-shaped clusters, about 5 cm (2 in.) wide, that ripen to small, ridged seeds about 3 mm (⅛ in.) long.

HOW TO GROW. Anise grows best in southern Europe. It is only successful in temperate regions in very hot summers because it is slow to germinate, requiring about four months to develop, and because its delicate roots do not take kindly to transplanting. However, seeds sown indoors in peat pots in early spring can be moved to the garden without shock when the weather becomes mild. Anise needs full sun; sow seeds in the spring when all danger of frost is past, covering them with 6 to 12 mm (¼ to ½ in.) of soil. If a few fast-growing radish seeds are sown with the slower-growing anise seeds they will help to mark the place in the garden. When seedlings are 5 cm (2 in.) tall, thin them to stand 20 cm (8 in.) apart. Keep them well watered, and draw the soil around the base of the plants to support their slender stems. Later, if flowers and seeds weigh down the stems, support them with stakes.

To harvest anise seeds, cut the plants when the stems are yellow and the seeds are grey-green. Wash the seed heads in warm water, drain on a towel and spread flat to dry in a warm, dark, well-ventilated place (seeds intended for future planting need not be washed). When completely dry, rub the seed heads between the palms to remove seeds from stems; store the seeds in an airtight container.

PORTULACA

P. oleracea (purslane)

Today, purslane is an almost forgotten herb in Britain although it was popular in Elizabethan days; in southern Europe, however, it is fairly common as a salad plant. Purslane is a sprawling annual that grows about 15 to 23 cm (6 to 9 in.) tall with a rosette of thick, succulent leaves. The leaves are bright green and oblong and are pulled when young; they may be cooked like spinach or used fresh in a salad; the variety *P. oleracea* ssp. *sativa* has golden leaves and can be used in the same way. In the Middle Ages purslane was used as a medicinal herb.

HOW TO GROW. Purslane is half-hardy in most parts of Europe and for a steady supply of leaves the plants need warm soil and full sun. Sow the seeds outdoors after all danger of frost is past, lightly covering them with soil. When the seedlings are large enough to be handled, thin them to 15 cm (6 in.) apart. For a continuous supply of salad greens, make successive sowings every month until July. Like spinach, purslane will keep on producing more leaves if the leaves are pulled as soon as they are ready.

POTERIUM See *Sanguisorba*

PRIMULA

P. veris, also called *P. officinalis* (cowslip)

A wild primrose, cowslip is a hardy perennial, growing 10 to 20 cm (4 to 8 in.) tall. Long, oval, crinkled leaves rise directly from the root, first appearing as a tight coil, then unfurling to form a rosette. The pale yellow, fragrant flowers are 12 mm ($\frac{1}{2}$ in.) wide. In earlier times, when the wild plant was more abundant than it is now, the blossoms were gathered to make cowslip wine and teas which had a sleep-inducing effect.

HOW TO GROW. Cowslip grows wild throughout temperate Europe and thrives in partial shade and a rich, porous, moist, acid soil (pH 5.0 to 6.0) supplemented with garden compost or leaf-mould. Choose a damp, shady spot where the plants will not be exposed to the midday sun. Cowslip can be started from seeds sown in a cold frame in late autumn or early spring; these will blossom when they are about one year old. To ensure blooms the first year, buy nursery plants in the spring. Set the young plants 15 to 30 cm (6 to 12 in.) apart, being careful to cover the entire root structure and the base of the stem. Cowslip thrives on frequent watering and the soil should not be allowed to dry out completely. If the summer is hot, keep the plants cool with a mulch of moss peat; in winter, protect them, in very cold areas, with bracken or straw. Cowslip can be increased by dividing the plant clumps in the spring immediately after they have flowered; this procedure also prevents overcrowding.

PYRETHRUM See *Chrysanthemum*

R

RORIPPA See *Nasturtium*

ROSA

R. damascena, also called *R. calendarum* and *R. gallica* var. *damascena* (damask rose, rose of Castile); *R. gallica* (French rose, rose of Provins)

The damask rose and French rose are hardy shrubs from whose petals and fruit, called rose hips, oils have been extracted since ancient times for use in medicines, perfumes and cooking. Both of these old roses are ancestors of many modern hybrids. *Rosa gallica* is a bush rose originally found in the Balkans and still grown there commercially for the volatile oil, attar of roses, distilled from its petals. During the Middle Ages, a rose-growing industry flourished in the small French town of Provins, inspiring *Rosa gallica*'s most frequently used common names. Apart from their use in perfumery and in pot-pourris, rose petals are also made into a diluted rose-water essence, used in flavouring sweet dishes and confectionery. Fresh petals can be floated on wine cups to perfume them, and in eastern Europe and Turkey rose petals are used in an exceedingly sweet jam or conserve which goes well with vanilla ice cream. In Europe, the petals are candied and crystallized and are used for the decoration of sweets and cakes; the petals are also sometimes used to flavour wine vinegars.

The damask rose usually grows 1.2 to 1.8 metres (4 to 6 ft) tall and (although it is technically a bush rose) resembles a climbing rose in character. Its branches are covered with large, hooked thorns and the grey-green, leaves are composed of five to seven toothed leaflets about 2.5 to 6 cm (1 to 2$\frac{1}{2}$ in.) long. Lush, semi-double flowers in pink, red or white bloom in early summer. The Rose des Quatre Saisons, *R. damascena* 'Semperflorens',

COWSLIP
Primula veris

DAMASK ROSE
Rosa damascena

133

FRENCH ROSE
Rosa gallica

ROSEMARY
Rosmarinus officinalis

also blossoms again in the autumn. The popular cultivar *R. damascena* 'Trigintipetala' has small, double, pink flowers. Although the damask rose is only slightly fragrant when fresh, its perfume increases when its petals are dried for use in potpourri.

The French rose grows 60 to 90 cm (2 to 3 ft) high and has stiff stems covered with bristles but is essentially thornless. Its leaves are composed of three to five, oval shaped leaflets with sharply toothed edges; each leaflet is deeply veined on top and has prickly hairs on the underside along the midrib. In early summer the French rose produces very fragrant flowers, 4 to 7.5 cm ($1\frac{1}{2}$ to 3 in.) wide, whose pink to crimson petals open from a disc-like centre filled with conspicuous yellow stamens.

HOW TO GROW. The damask and French roses grow in all parts of Europe except for extremely cold northern regions. They prefer full sun and good, well-drained garden soil supplemented with garden compost or manure. They can be planted in the autumn or spring. Choose a separate bed for them away from the entangling roots of other shrubs and trees and space the bushes 1 to 1.2 metres (3 to 4 ft) apart. Dig a hole 60 cm (2 ft) deep and wide, discarding all but the topsoil. Mix well-rotted manure, garden compost and topsoil and make a cone-shaped mound in the bottom of the hole. Place the rose bush on this hill, spreading the roots out as much as possible (cut off any damaged roots). Fill the space around the roots with soil halfway up; water. Continue to fill the hole, firming down the soil.

After autumn planting in areas where winter temperatures go below −12°C (10°F), cover the newly set plants with a protective mulch of bracken or straw. When the ground thaws the following spring, remove this winter protection. After the bushes are established, feed them twice a year, in early spring and again in early summer, using a special rose fertilizer hoed into the soil in a 60 cm (2 ft) circle around each plant. To conserve moisture, prevent weed growth and keep the roots cool, cover the soil with a mulch of moss peat or grass clippings. Prune bushes every spring; first remove all the dead wood and injured branches, then trim the remaining branches. Severe pruning, however, will limit the number of flowers because the shrubs will expend their energies in growing new branches. Additional bushes can be propagated from suckers taken during the spring or from stem cuttings in early summer.

To harvest rose petals for culinary use, collect them when the flowers are unfolding; or gather on a dry morning for potpourris. Spread them flat on a frame covered with muslin and dry them in a well-ventilated, shaded place, turning them every day. If the petals are not dry in three or four days, they can be dehydrated further in a barely warm oven with the door left ajar. To harvest rose hips, cut them after they have turned red in the autumn.

ROSMARINUS
R. officinalis (rosemary)

Rosemary, the herb of remembrance, is a slightly tender, shrubby evergreen cultivated for its richly aromatic leaves, which are used fresh or dried in cooking. A native of the Mediterranean, where it grows wild on rocky hillsides, its fragrance is so intense that during the harvest season when the wind is right, it can be smelt 32 km (20 miles) out at sea. Rosemary usually grows 60 to 90 cm (2 to 3 ft) high but in Mediterranean areas it can become 1.5 to 1.8 metres (5 to 6 ft) tall. Its spiky, evergreen leaves are 2 to 5 cm ($\frac{3}{4}$ to 2 in.) long and grey-green with faint white lines on the undersides. During the spring and early summer, and infrequently at other seasons, the woody stems bear pale-blue blossoms, 12 mm ($\frac{1}{2}$ in.) in diameter, which are attractive to bees. Sprigs of rosemary impart an aromatic flavour to roast meats, especially lamb and veal, game and strongly flavoured fish; it is a favourite herb in Italian cooking and combines particularly well with garlic.

HOW TO GROW. Rosemary is fully hardy only in its native Mediterranean regions, but it survives average winters as far north as southern Britain. Elsewhere, it is grown in pots that can be taken indoors over the winter. It grows best in full sun but will tolerate partial shade, and it thrives in a well-drained soil with a pH of 6.0 to 7.5; wet soil inhibits its growth. Although rosemary can be grown from seed, germination is extremely slow and it takes as long as three years to produce a sizeable plant. Consequently, most gardeners buy their first plant, then start new plants from stem cuttings. For cuttings, clip a sprig of firm new growth, 10 to 12.5 cm (4 to 5 in.) long, from the top of the plant, strip the bottom 4 cm ($1\frac{1}{2}$ in.) of leaves, and stick the sprig in wet sand until it has rooted; cuttings are often slow to root. Rosemary can also be propagated by layering or pinning down the lower rambling branches against the soil until roots form, making new plants.

When planting rosemary in the garden, space it 60 to 90 cm (2 to 3 ft) apart to encourage bushy growth. When planting it in a pot, choose a pot the size of the roots; rosemary does best when its roots are somewhat crowded. Use a proprietary potting compost.

Indoor-grown rosemary needs at least five hours of direct sunlight a day, or 12 hours of strong artificial light. The soil must never be allowed to dry out completely, but it should be allowed to become moderately dry between deep waterings. Indoors, the plant grows slowly and seldom reaches a height of more than 60 cm (2 ft).

Rosemary leaves can be cut for use fresh at any time. When harvesting for drying, their flavour is best just before the plant blooms. Spread the cut stems on a screen and dry them in a dark, well-ventilated place; then store leaves and stems in an airtight container.

RUMEX
R. scutatus (sorrel)

Sorrel is a hardy perennial cultivated for its light green, spear-shaped leaves that have a mildly sour, lemony taste. Picked when young and tender, they add zest to salads, and more mature leaves can be cooked and eaten like spinach or as a purée filling for omelettes. Chopped sorrel leaves, with other herbs, are used in classic stuffings for strong-flavoured fish, such as salmon and eels. The plant grows 45 to 60 cm ($1\frac{1}{2}$ to 2 ft) high and the leaves form dense clusters of foliage. Panicles of yellowish-green flowers bloom in the spring followed by reddish seeds that are great favourites of finches. Like wild dock, a close relative, sorrel has roots that grow deep into the soil and are difficult to eradicate once established.

HOW TO GROW. Sorrel grows in most parts of Europe, including Britain, though, except in France, it is a much neglected herb. It does best in sun but will tolerate partial shade; it will grow in any rich, moist soil. Sow seeds outdoors in spring, covering them with 6 mm ($\frac{1}{4}$ in.) of soil. When the seedlings are 2.5 to 5 cm (1 to 2 in.) tall, thin or transplant them to stand 15 to 20 cm (6 to 8 in.) apart. Remove flower heads and stems as soon as they appear, to encourage leaf growth and to prevent seed formation. If you do allow the plants to go to seed, be ready to pull up unwanted seedlings. Sorrel will quickly seed itself, sometimes producing new plants in the same year the seeds fall. It spreads rapidly and is difficult to control. In hot weather sorrel leaves may turn bitter; a mulch around the bases of

SORREL
Rumex scutatus

the plants will help to prevent this by conserving moisture. But if bitterness should develop, the mild flavour of the leaves will return when the weather becomes cooler.

Sorrel grows well indoors provided it has at least five hours of strong, direct sunlight a day and plenty of water. It should be grown in deep containers to accommodate its long roots. Use a proprietary potting compost and feed with liquid fertilizer at half the recommended strength every two weeks. Water plants frequently enough to keep the soil from becoming completely dry. If leaves begin to curl, check them for mites, which can be treated by washing the leaves in a mild solution of soap and water. Indoor-grown sorrel reaches a height of only 20 cm (8 in.).

RUTA

R. graveolens (rue, herb of grace)

Rue is a musky-smelling—to many people obnoxious— evergreen perennial cultivated for its attractive blue-green foliage and yellow blossoms, and for its seed pods, which are dried for use in ornamental arrangements. In Greek and Roman times it was a culinary and medicinal herb, but it should be used in cooking only in very small quantities, with, for example, fish and egg dishes. But be very wary, since many people are allergic to it, and it can be poisonous if taken in large quantities. Commercially, one variety of rue is used in the production of the bitter-tasting Italian liqueur, grappa.

The bushy plant, 30 to 90 cm (1 to 3 ft) high and wide, has 7.5 to 12.5 cm (3 to 5 in.) leaves segmented into oval lobes, and 2 cm ($\frac{3}{4}$ in.) flowers consisting of four or five wide-spreading petals; these bloom in terminal clusters from midsummer to autumn. For garden decoration, the cultivar 'Jackman's Blue' has more intense blue-green leaves.

HOW TO GROW. Rue is hardy in temperate and southern Europe. It thrives in full sun but will tolerate partial shade and does best in well-drained, sandy, slightly alkaline soil with a pH of 7.0 to 7.5. Sow seeds outdoors in the spring or late summer, or start seeds indoors in pots in late winter for transplanting outdoors when all danger of frost is past. Thin or transplant seedlings to stand 30 to 45 cm (1 to $1\frac{1}{2}$ ft) apart when they are 5 to 7.5 cm (2 to 3 in.) high. After flowers bloom the first time, cut off the flower heads and spread garden compost or manure around the bases of the plants to encourage a second flowering. Mature rue should be trimmed back to half its size, or even to just above ground level, every other spring to encourage full, bushy growth. The plant will seed itself; it can also be propagated, although with considerable difficulty, from stem cuttings in early summer.

S

SALVIA

S. officinalis (sage, garden sage); *S. sclarea* (clary)

Sage, a shrubby evergreen, whose distinctive grey-green foliage has added "sage green" to the palette of colours, makes a handsome addition to the garden and a common source of flavouring for the kitchen. The flavour of the leaves, fresh or dried, is slightly pungent and combines best with strong meats, such as pork, goose and sausages. In Germany it is popular with fish dishes, and in Mediterranean countries small game birds are wrapped in sage leaves for roasting. Sage's lesser known relative, clary, is a biennial often grown as an annual. It can be used to flavour soups and meat stews; the highly aromatic, somewhat bitter leaves are used commercially in the perfumery industry, and were formerly a popular flavouring for wines of the muscatel type.

Sage reaches a height of 45 to 75 cm (1½ to 2½ ft) with a tendency to sprawl if not trimmed, while clary grows as tall as 90 cm (3 ft). The tiny, lilac-blue flowers of sage bloom on terminal spikes in the summer, and its wrinkled, spear-shaped leaves, 5 to 10 cm (2 to 4 in.) long, grow opposite each other on stiff, hairy stems. After a plant's second year, two harvests—sometimes three—can be had in a season. The flower spikes of clary are bluish-white with prominent purple bracts; they bloom in late summer. Its leaves are light green, pointed, oval and downy. It makes a decorative plant for the annual border.

HOW TO GROW. Sage and clary are both hardy in most parts of Europe. Both thrive in any well-drained garden soil with a pH of 5.5 to 6.5. They do best in full sun, but will also grow in light shade. Sage grown from seed takes two years to reach maturity, so it is usually purchased as nursery stock or propagated from stem cuttings in early summer. If sage is to be grown from seed, sow in the early spring, covering the seeds with 6 mm (¼ in.) of soil. Thin seedlings or set nursery stock to stand 45 to 60 cm (1½ to 2 ft) apart. Each spring, cut back the previous year's growth by half, and every four or five years, as plants get woody, divide the root clumps in the early spring and re-plant them in soil enriched with garden compost or manure.

Sage leaves can be picked any time to use fresh. To store them, harvest young leaves from late spring to early autumn, cutting 15 to 20 cm (6 to 8 in.) pieces from the tips of the stems just as the flower buds appear. Sometimes a third harvest is also possible but, to avoid leaving the plant vulnerable to cold, do not harvest sage after early autumn. To dry the leaves, hang them in the shade for about a week or dry them in a cool oven, then store them in airtight containers. Sage and clary do not grow well indoors.

SANGUISORBA

S. minor also called *Poterium sanguisorba* (burnet, salad burnet)

Burnet is an old-fashioned herb whose delicate cucumber-flavoured leaves were once popular in cooling drinks; the young leaves are used in salads and as a flavouring for sauces. It is a hardy perennial growing 30 to 60 cm (1 to 2 ft) high, with compound leaves about 2 cm (¾ in.) long, which resemble the leaves of the wild rose. They spread in a rosette from the base of the plant, forming a clump 45 to 60 cm (1½ to 2 ft) across. In early summer, thimble-shaped, 12 mm (½ in.) tufts of greenish flowers with purple-red stamens, giving an overall reddish appearance, bloom on reddish-brown stems. Burnet may spread in the garden if its seeds are allowed to ripen.

HOW TO GROW. Burnet is hardy throughout Europe, thriving on chalky soils. It is almost an evergreen, its lower leaves staying green all winter. It needs full sun and grows best in well-drained soil with a pH of 6.0 to 8.0. Sow seeds in the open ground in the late autumn or early spring, covering them with 12 mm (½ in.) of soil. Thin seedlings to stand 30 to 38 cm (1 to 1¼ ft) apart. If the soil is rich and growth is strong, it is a good idea to divide roots and replant the divisions early each spring. To main-tain a constant supply of tender young leaves for eating, cut off old foliage and flower stalks to stimulate the pro-duction of new leaves. Burnet leaves can be harvested for use fresh until covered by snow and they may also be frozen.

Burnet grown indoors as a pot plant requires at least five hours of direct sunlight a day. Start with seedlings brought in from the garden, using a standard potting compost. Trim off old leaves from time to time to keep the plant compact. Indoor-grown burnet grows more slowly and is smaller than the garden-grown plant.

CLARY
Salvia sclarea

BURNET
Sanguisorba minor

COTTON LAVENDER
Santolina chamaecyparissus

SUMMER SAVORY
Satureja hortensis

SANTOLINA
S. chamaecyparissus also called *S. incana* and *S. tomentosa* (cotton lavender)

Cotton lavender is a hardy, shrubby perennial, 30 to 60 cm (1 to 2 ft) tall, cultivated for its decorative, pungent, silver-grey leaves whose scent is particularly noticeable when the foliage is rubbed. The leaves can be used in sachets, and the plant is also suitable for a low, fragrant hedge round a herb plot. The fern-like foliage, 2.5 to 4 cm (1 to 1½ in.) long, branches out to create a shrubby appearance, and bushes are often wider than they are tall. They are frequently grown as an element in formal gardens, in contrast to the green foliage of *S. virens.* If not pruned for such a purpose, cotton lavender bears 2 cm (¾ in.) button-shaped, yellow flowers in early summer on slender, leafless stems.

HOW TO GROW. Cotton lavender is hardy in most parts of Europe though less so in cold northern regions where it can be treated as an annual. It needs full sun and will grow in almost any well-drained soil. It resists salt sprays and is a good seaside plant. Cotton lavender is easily propagated from stem cuttings taken in the summer, overwintered in a cold frame and set outside the following spring. Stem cuttings are slow to reach full size, taking as long as two years to mature. Larger plants of cotton lavender can be produced by layering stems in the autumn and dividing the rooted stems in the spring. Mature plants should be clipped back by half or more annually in the spring, and, if the plants are being grown solely for their foliage, again in midsummer to prevent flowering. In regions where winter temperatures remain below freezing for long periods, mulch the plants with bracken or straw.

Cotton lavender grown indoors as a pot plant needs at least five hours a day of direct sunlight and good ventilation. It tolerates temperatures as low as freezing and does well in any proprietary potting compost. Indoors, plants can be trained to form miniature bushes, but they require regular pruning to retain compactness; they rarely grow more than 25 to 30 cm (10 to 12 in.) high indoors. Allow the soil to become nearly dry between waterings.

SAROTHAMNUS See *Cytisus*

SATUREJA
S. hortensis (summer savory); *S. montana* (winter savory)

Summer savory and winter savory are two peppery-tasting seasoning herbs used to flavour meats, sauces and stuffings and, in France and Germany in particular, young beans and peas. The two savories resemble each other with their straggly, bush-like growth and weak, woody, branching stems. Both bear whorls of insignificant pink, lavender-blue or white flowers from midsummer to autumn, luring bees with their fragrant perfume. The bitter, tangy flavour and scent of the savories, however, are strongest before the flowers appear.

Summer savory, an annual, is sweeter tasting and less pungent than its perennial relative, winter savory. Its narrow, lance-shaped leaves, 1.2 to 4 cm (½ to 1½ in.) long, are covered with short, downy hairs and grow sparsely in pairs along stems 30 to 45 cm (1 to 1½ ft) high. Unless harvested, this foliage turns red deepening to purple in late summer. Summer savory is commonly picked in the summer before its flowers open; one or two plants will be sufficient for the needs of most families. If the plants are allowed to flower and set seeds, they quickly multiply through self-sown seedlings.

Winter savory, a perennial, is a slightly smaller and

wider plant than summer savory. It reaches a height of 30 cm (1 ft) and sprawls to an equal width. Its narrow, pointed leaves, only 2 mm ($\frac{1}{16}$ in.) wide, are smooth and shiny, and its flowers tend to be deeper hued than those of summer savory. The leaves remain green throughout the winter in mild climates.

HOW TO GROW. Summer and winter savory both like full sun and ordinary, not particularly fertile, well-drained soil. Start summer savory from seeds sown about 6 mm ($\frac{1}{4}$ in.) deep in the early spring, and, for a constant supply of fresh leaves, make successive sowings at intervals of three to four weeks. Germination takes about 14 to 21 days. Thin seedlings to stand 10 to 15 cm (4 to 6 in.) apart; close spacing helps to keep the top-heavy plants from falling over. Later, when the plants are taller, mound soil around their bases to keep them upright. Fresh leaves can be cut for use at any time.

Winter savory, native to southern Europe, is generally hardy in temperate regions. Its seeds are slow to germinate, so the plants are commonly started from root divisions or stem cuttings taken in the spring, or by layering. Set plants in the ground in early spring, spacing them 30 cm (1 ft) apart. When they are 15 cm (6 in.) tall, pinch back tops to encourage bushy growth. Remove dead wood whenever it appears, and in frost-prone areas clip back the plants in the autumn to 7.5 to 15 cm (3 to 6 in.) above the ground; cover each plant with a mulch of bracken or straw after the ground freezes. Winter savory plants need to be divided and replanted every two or three years to achieve satisfactory growth.

Both summer and winter savory should·be harvested for drying before the flowers bloom. Cut summer savory down to the ground or pull it up by the roots; cut only the tender tip growth of winter savory. Hang both types upside down in bunches to dry in a paper bag, or lay them flat on a muslin-covered tray in a dark, well-ventilated room. When the leaves are thoroughly dry, rub the bag so that the leaves fall to the bottom; or rub the leafstalks between the hands. Store them in an airtight container.

Both species can be grown indoors in pots or window boxes provided they get at least five hours of direct sunlight a day. Start with young plants or bring mature plants in from the garden in late summer. Use a standard potting compost. At the time of potting, cut back winter savory to half its size, and allow it to recover outdoors for two or three weeks. Allow the soil around both savories to become moderately dry between waterings, and feed them with a general liquid fertilizer, used at half the recommended strength, at intervals of three to four weeks. Leaves may be cut as needed but winter savory should be trimmed sparingly in the winter because its rate of recovery after pruning is slower then.

SEMPERVIVUM
S. tectorum (houseleek, hen-and-chickens, St Patrick's cabbage)

The houseleek is a succulent perennial once grown as a home remedy for warts, fevers and bruises of the skin, and planted on rooftops in the belief that it prevented lightning and thunder. The fleshy, wedge-shaped leaves edged with bristly, white hairs form small, cabbage-like rosettes 5 to 10 cm (2 to 4 in.) across. Each mature rosette is surrounded by smaller ones that rise as offshoots, hence the other common name, hen-and-chickens. The moisture-storing leaves enable the plants to survive during the driest weather. In midsummer, a flower spike rises from the centre of each mature rosette, reaching a height of about 23 cm (9 in.). As the pinkish-red blooms fade, the main

WINTER SAVORY
Satureja montana

HOUSELEEK
Sempervivum tectorum

SESAME
Sesamum indicum

WHITE MUSTARD
Sinapis alba

rosette dies, but new rosettes continue to grow to keep a colony of plants thriving for many years.

HOW TO GROW. Houseleek grows throughout Europe. It needs well-drained soil and is usually planted in rock gardens or in raised beds. You can plant offsets at any time, spacing them 15 to 23 cm (6 to 9 in.) apart; plants spread quickly through new offsets to fill open spaces. Fertilizer is rarely needed and may even cause abnormal growth.

Houseleek can be grown indoors like cactus in a sunny window. Plant it in a compost that is not too rich, such as 3 parts loam, 2 parts coarse sand and 1 part peat or leaf-mould. Keep the soil barely moist during the active growing season, and allow it to become nearly dry during the winter rest period.

SESAMUM
S. indicum, also called *S. orientale* (sesame, semsem)

Sesame is a tropical annual cultivated in Asia and Africa for its oil and for its oily, nut-flavoured seeds which are used whole in cakes, biscuits and bread, or ground as an ingredient in Middle Eastern cooking; ground sesame paste known as *tahina* makes an excellent base for an hors d'oeuvre dip. Sesame reaches a height of up to 1.8 metres (6 ft), and its leaves are 7.5 to 12.5 cm (3 to 5 in.) long. Throughout the summer it produces 2.5 cm (1 in.) long, trumpet-shaped, white flowers with pink, yellow or pale violet markings. The seed pods form inside the faded flowers and when fully ripened suddenly burst open, scattering the seeds. (The magic password "open sesame", used by Ali Baba in the *Arabian Nights* tale, probably originated from this trait.)

HOW TO GROW. A native and staple of India and China, sesame needs four months of near tropical weather for the seeds to mature, so it can be grown in Europe only in warm Mediterranean countries, usually as a curiosity. Sesame needs full sun and will grow in almost any well-drained soil. Sow seeds 6 mm ($\frac{1}{4}$ in.) deep in late spring when night temperatures remain above 15°C (60°F), or sow indoors in pots or trays in late winter, for transfer to the open garden. Thin seedlings or transplant pot-grown plants to stand 15 to 20 cm (6 to 8 in.) apart. To harvest, cut the stems off at ground level before the oldest pods begin to open and drop them in a paper bag until the seed pods dry and release their seeds. Store in an airtight container.

SINAPIS
S. alba, also known as *Brassica alba* (white mustard, yellow mustard)

The white mustard plant, a 25 to 60 cm (10 to 24 in.) tall annual topped with clusters of bright yellow flowers, spreads so readily it can be a nuisance. It is cultivated commercially for the pale yellow seeds, which are crushed to make table mustard; so many seeds are required, however, that it is impracticable for home gardeners to grow it for this purpose. Young leaves make a peppery flavouring for salads and are sometimes cooked as greens.

The bright green leaves of the mustard plant reach a length of 20 cm (8 in.), decreasing in size as they ascend the stem; the four-petalled, yellow flowers that cluster at the top are each about 12 mm ($\frac{1}{2}$ in.) across. The seed pod contains four to eight seeds, each about 2 mm ($\frac{1}{16}$ in.) wide.

HOW TO GROW. White mustard does best in full sun and will grow in almost any well-drained soil. Sow seeds in early spring or late summer; the plants will be large enough to harvest in approximately two months. If grown during midsummer, the foliage is too strong for most tastes. Mustard greens can also be grown indoors to be eaten as seedlings; sow them in a shallow container of potting compost. When the seedlings are 4 cm (1½ in.) tall, cut them off close to the soil. (See also *Lepidium*.)

SIUM
S. sisarum (skirret)

Skirret is a perennial with a multiple root that tastes something like sweet parsnip (it is related to the wild water parsnip) and is sometimes grown as a vegetable. It reaches a height of 60 to 120 cm (2 to 4 ft) and has sharply toothed, compound leaves having three to seven leaflets, 1.2 to 2.5 cm (½ to 1 in.) long. In early summer it bears umbrella-shaped heads of tiny, white flowers about 2.5 cm (1 in.) across. The long, tapering roots grow in clusters like dahlia tubers but are joined at the top. One plant produces many roots.

HOW TO GROW. Skirret is hardy in temperate Europe, including Britain and does best in a rich, well-drained garden soil with a pH of 6.0 to 8.0. For a vegetable crop it should be raised annually from seeds sown 12 mm (½ in.) deep in the spring. Skirret can also be grown from root divisions, planted in the early spring and spaced 20 to 30 cm (8 to 12 in.) apart to be grown for ornamental purposes. If growing skirret for table use, cut back the flower heads before they turn to seed to encourage root growth. Since the roots, like parsnips, will withstand freezing, they will not be harmed by remaining in the ground, although they can also be dug up and stored in sand.

SPIRAEA See *Filipendula*

STACHYS
S. officinalis (wood betony, bishop's wort, woundwort); *S. olympica*, also called *S. lanata* (lamb's ears, woolly betony, donkey's ears)

During the Middle Ages these two perennial herbs were grown for their large leaves which were used for bandaging wounds, hence the name woundwort. Wood betony was also used for herbal teas and as a flavouring in home-brewed beers. Today, both are cultivated for their ornamental value—wood betony for its flowers, lamb's ears as a ground cover. Except for the fact that their flowers bloom in spikes, the two plants do not at all resemble each other.

Wood betony grows 30 to 90 cm (1 to 3 ft) tall and its hairy, heart-shaped leaves are 5 to 10 cm (2 to 4 in.) long with deeply wrinkled surfaces and coarse-toothed edges. In midsummer, it produces flowering spikes densely filled with bell-shaped blossoms that are good for cutting. The triangular seeds, enclosed in brown pods that drop to the ground, seed themselves in the autumn. The entire plant is strongly aromatic.

Lamb's ears, a smaller plant, 30 to 45 cm (1 to 1½ ft) tall, is named for its soft, downy foliage that strongly resembles the silky texture of young animal ears. The texture of these large, elongated, grey-green leaves, 7.5 to 15 cm (3 to 6 in.) long and 2.5 to 4 cm (1 to 1½ in.) wide, comes from a covering of soft woolly hairs. The flower spikes of lamb's ears, which bloom in early summer, rise about 15 cm (6 in.) above the foliage on strong stems; unlike those of wood betony, they are not striking.

HOW TO GROW. Both herbs can be grown throughout Europe, though less successfully in hot Mediterranean climates. They thrive in full sun and a well-drained garden soil. Although they may be started from seeds sown in the spring, the plants take two years to mature. Consequently they are usually grown from root divisions planted in the

SKIRRET
Sium sisarum

WOOD BETONY
Stachys officinalis

141

LAMB'S EARS
Stachys olympica

COMFREY
Symphytum officinale

early spring or autumn, spaced 30 to 45 cm (1 to 1½ ft) apart. Plants spread to form a compact mass and need little care. If the flower spikes are cut back after flowering, new blossoms will keep reappearing until the first frost. Divide plant clumps every two or three years to prevent overcrowding.

SYMPHYTUM
S. officinale (comfrey, knit-bone, blackwort)

Comfrey is a hardy perennial frequently found growing wild, but less often seen in the herb garden. Its uses are similar to those of borage; the young leaves, which combine the flavours of endive and asparagus, can be eaten as a salad green. Comfrey is said to have great healing powers, hence the common name knit-bone, and comfrey ointment is still made and sold by herbalists and health shops. Some farmers grow comfrey for composting, ploughing it back as enrichment for the soil. It is a sturdy plant, reaching a height of 60 to 105 cm (2 to 3½ ft) with very large, hairy lower leaves, as much as 38 to 50 cm (1¼ to 1¾ ft) long; the leaves are smaller in size higher up the flower-bearing stem. Beginning in late spring, 2 cm (¾ in.) long, bell-shaped flowers of yellow, mauve, blue or white bloom in arched sprays on slender stems and keep flowering for most of the summer. Each flower produces four seeds which ripen in a cup-shaped fruit.

HOW TO GROW. Comfrey is hardy in all parts of Europe. It does best in full sun but tolerates partial shade: it thrives in any moist, fairly rich garden soil. It is usually grown from root divisions or from root cuttings taken in the spring or autumn. Plant the root sections horizontally, 7.5 to 15 cm (3 to 6 in.) deep and 0.9 to 1.2 metres (3 to 4 ft) apart, away from smaller herbs. To encourage leaf growth, cut off the flower sprays when they appear. Although leaves may be harvested from the first year on, the best yields are in the third year. Cut leaves when the plants are 30 to 45 cm (1 to 1½ ft) high, just before they bloom. Cut no lower than 5 cm (2 in.) from the ground, so as not to injure the root crown of the plant. Fresh leaves are the most desirable, but leaves may be dried for later use; dry them for 2 to 3 days in a cool, dark place, then crush them between your palms and store them in an airtight container.

T

TANACETUM
T. vulgare, also called *Chrysanthemum vulgare* (tansy, bitter buttons, alecost)

Tansy is a hardy perennial 60 to 90 cm (2 to 3 ft) tall whose pungent, bitter-tasting leaves were a favourite flavouring in the Middle Ages and later in custards and other sweet puddings; they were also used in fish dishes and meat stuffings. The word tansy has survived in Britain as a term for old-fashioned fruit purées mixed with eggs and cream. Today, tansy is grown in the ornamental garden, and the flowers are used for dried flower arrangements. It is a decorative plant, noted for its deeply cut, fern-like leaves, 7.5 to 12.5 cm (3 to 5 in.) long, and for its clusters of yellow, button-shaped, petalless flowers, 6 mm (¼ in.) wide, which bloom in mid to late summer. The flowers are long-lasting and so are the flat-topped seed heads that follow them; they remain on the plant through the winter and seed themselves the following spring. In the garden, tansy can be invasive, its creeping roots quickly taking over more than their allotted space.

HOW TO GROW. Tansy is native to Europe, hardy in all areas, and often found in the wild. It does best in full sun but will tolerate shade; although it will grow in almost any soil, it is especially luxuriant in a relatively moist, loamy soil. Sow seeds in early spring or autumn or start plants from root divisions in the early spring, spacing them 30 to 60 cm (1 to 2 ft) apart. Place tansy against a wall or fence to help protect the long stems from blowing in wind and rain; if not grown against a fence, mature plants may need to be staked. Because tansy spreads rapidly, it should be given an isolated position or should be planted in a sunken open-ended metal bucket that will constrict the wandering roots. If the flower heads are cut off before they seed, tansy can be encouraged to produce a hedge-like growth. To dry the flowers for winter arrangements, cut stems of yellow buttons just after they have opened, and hang them in loose bunches upside down in a cool, dark place with good ventilation.

TARAXACUM

T. officinale, also called *Leontodon taraxacum* (dandelion)

Suggested to gardeners with misgivings, this well-known weed, so often considered a troublesome nuisance in the garden and lawn, is actually a valuable salad herb, rich in vitamins A, B, C and D. The wild plant is somewhat bitter, but cultivated varieties specially bred for table use have a sweeter taste. The young, tender leaves are especially popular, either in a salad or cooked like spinach, and the root—like the root of its close relative chicory—can be roasted as a substitute for coffee. The flowers are used in home-winemaking, and both leaves and roots are also used as a flavouring in herbal beers.

Dandelion is a perennial, 5 to 30 cm (2 to 12 in.) tall whose deeply serrated, dark green leaves inspired the French name "dent de lion", or lion's tooth. Its golden-yellow flowers, among the first to appear in the spring, bloom on solitary, hollow stems, and quickly turn to fluffy puff balls, scattering hundreds of seeds in the wind. Seeds germinate in only three days, which explains the plant's rapid proliferation. The deep-reaching taproot is difficult to eradicate and requires special tools or weed killers.

HOW TO GROW. Dandelion is hardy throughout Europe and adapts to any soil conditions, including very poor ones. However, to produce the most tender leaves, grow cultivated varieties in rich, moist soil. Sow dandelion seeds in the spring or autumn in an isolated part of the garden where they can be controlled, or transplant clumps to a spot where they can be kept under cultivation. Cut flower heads before they open to increase the plant's production of salad greens and to avoid self-seeding in other parts of the garden. The tender leaves can be cut at any time, but their flavour is best in the spring when they first appear. One plant may be harvested several times during its five-month growing season.

TEUCRIUM

T. chamaedrys (germander, wall germander)

Once used as a home remedy against gout, germander is grown today as a ground cover or border plant. It spreads rapidly from creeping roots and rises above the ground in tufts only 15 to 45 cm (6 in. to 1½ ft) high. Its woody, branching, upright stems bear shiny, dark green, oval leaves, 1.2 to 4 cm (½ to 1½ in.) long, scalloped along the edges and covered with tiny hairs. The 2 cm (¾ in.), speckled, bright pink flowers are tubular, with upper and lower lips. They grow in whorls consisting of about six blossoms at the point where the leaves join the stem, and bloom from midsummer onwards. Germander is often planted as a low hedge because it responds well to clipping.

HOW TO GROW. Germander is hardy in all parts of

TANSY
Tanacetum vulgare

DANDELION
Taraxacum officinale

GERMANDER
Teucrium chamaedrys

Europe with the exception of very cold and exposed northern regions. It does best in full sun but will tolerate partial shade and thrives in any well-drained, fairly rich, light-textured soil. Seeds are extremely slow to germinate, taking up to 30 days, so the easiest way to propagate is from root divisions. Set rooted cuttings or root divisions in the garden in the spring, spacing them 30 cm (1 ft) apart along a border, or tuck individual plants into wall crevices or between paving stones. Cut back the leaf tips and woody stems every spring to encourage new growth.

THYMUS

T. x *citriodorus* (lemon thyme); *T. serpyllum* (wild thyme, creeping thyme); *T. vulgaris* (common thyme, garden thyme)

An essential ingredient in the cook's most basic *bouquet garni*, thyme has been cultivated since the days of ancient Greece for its strongly aromatic, slightly pungent foliage. It is one of the most important and best of all culinary herbs, used for flavouring soups and vegetables, meat, poultry and game dishes, fish and pickling vinegars. It is used in herbal teas and has also been employed medicinally including its use as an antiseptic. Lemon thyme, in addition, flavours fruit dishes and custards. The low, shrubby perennials in this large genus of more than 100 species vary from 2.5 to 30 cm (1 to 12 in.) in height and can be differentiated by the size and intensity of their scented leaves and the upright or reclining position of their stems. All thymes have thin, woody, twig-like stems with small, shiny oval-shaped leaves approximately 6 to 12 mm ($\frac{1}{4}$ to $\frac{1}{2}$ in.) long. In the early summer, pale rose to lilac-coloured flowers appear at the ends of the stems or in whorls where the upper leaves join the stem. The tiny seeds keep their germinating power for up to three years.

Common thyme and lemon thyme are popular for cooking while wild thyme is chiefly grown as an ornamental garden plant. Common thyme, the tallest of the three, also has the strongest scent and flavour; it forms upright bushes 15 to 30 cm (6 to 12 in.) high. There are three principal types of common thyme: English or variegated-leaf thyme; German or broad-leaf thyme; and French or narrow-leaf thyme. Each of these varieties is distinguished, as its name indicates, by the shape of its leaves.

Lemon thyme closely resembles common thyme except for its intense lemon scent. Its leaves are slightly broader and its stems semi-trailing. One cultivar of lemon thyme 'Aureus' has yellowish-green leaves and grows only 15 cm (6 in.) high; it is used as a fragrant ground cover.

Wild thyme, sometimes called mother-of-thyme because it is thought to be one of the original thymes, is a creeping, delicate-looking but tough species cultivated for its aromatic, carpet-like growth, which is especially suited to rock gardens and terraces; its tiny, erect flowering stems rise only 2.5 to 7.5 cm (1 to 3 in.) high. The numerous named cultivars of wild thyme differ in flower colour and the size and shape of the leaves; they include the tiny, white *T. serpyllum* 'Albus', the pink-flowered 'Annie Hall', the crimson-white blossomed 'Coccineus' and the woolly, grey-leaved 'Lanuginosus'.

HOW TO GROW. All thymes, which are native to Europe, are fully hardy, and the culinary types also do well indoors. They thrive in full sun and grow best in light, well-drained soil with a pH of 5.5 to 7.0. Plants can be grown from seeds sown 6 mm ($\frac{1}{4}$ in.) deep outdoors in the spring or started indoors in pots or seed trays. But germination is slow—thyme requires about two years to reach a usable size—and the herb is commonly grown from root divisions made in the spring or stem cuttings taken at any time.

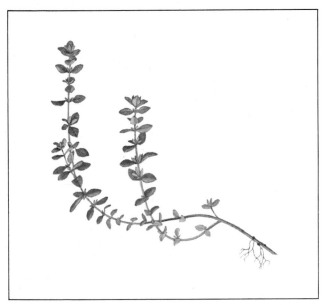

LEMON THYME
Thymus x *citriodorus*

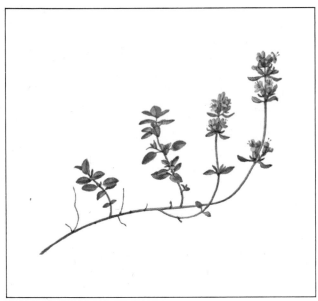

WILD THYME
Thymus serpyllum

Wild thyme can, in addition, be propagated by layering. Space common and lemon thyme 30 cm (1 ft) apart; tuck wild thyme between rocks, bricks or flagstones, or, if using it as a ground cover, space plants 25 cm (10 in.) apart. Scatter a tablespoon of bone-meal around the base of each plant in spring and hoe this supplement into the soil. Do not feed again until the following spring because fast growth makes plants susceptible to frost damage.

In early spring, trim the stems of lemon and common thyme back to half of the previous year's growth to encourage dense growth. In areas where winter temperatures remain below zero for extended periods, apply a winter mulch of bracken over the plants in the late autumn after the ground freezes. Thyme becomes woody and less fragrant after several years unless young growth is encouraged by spring pruning; it should ideally be replaced after three or four years.

Leaves can be picked in small quantities for fresh use at any time. To harvest the herb for drying, cut the stems back just before or at the time of flowering and hang upside down in bunches to dry in a dark, well-ventilated place. Strip the leaves from the stems when dry and store in an airtight container. The flowers can also be dried for fragrant sachets and potpourris. When harvesting thyme in late summer, do not remove more than a third of the stem, so that the plant is not encouraged to make tender growth that may not survive the winter.

Lemon and common thyme grown indoors as pot plants require at least five hours of strong, direct sunlight a day. They do best in potting composts that approximate to their gravelly outdoor environment; proprietary potting compost should be supplemented with lime chips or coarse sand. Plant different types in several containers for a steady supply of thyme, choosing pots according to the size of the plants. Keep the stem tips well pruned to encourage bushy growth. Wild thyme does not usually thrive indoors. Water all plants until moist but not soggy, and allow the soil to dry between waterings.

TRIGONELLA

T. foenum-graecum (fenugreek, bird's-foot, Greek hayseed)

One of the oldest and most widely used herbs in India, fenugreek is cultivated for its celery-flavoured seeds, which are an ingredient in curries and chutneys; the leaves, though bitter, are often curried, and quite young leaves make an unusual addition to a green salad.

Fenugreek is an annual and a member of the pea family. It grows 30 to 60 cm (1 to 2 ft) tall and its 2.5 to 5 cm (1 to 2 in.), oval leaves are attached in groups of three to upright, hollow stems. In its early stages of growth the plant resembles sweet clover. Beginning early in the summer and continuing for several months, very fragrant, off-white flowers, 1.2 to 2.5 cm ($\frac{1}{2}$ to 1 in.) long, bloom at the leaf axils. These are followed by pointed seed pods up to 15 cm (6 in.) long, which resemble French beans but grow upright; each pod contains about 16 brown seeds.

HOW TO GROW. Fenugreek flowers and seeds only in Mediterranean climates, but farther north it can be grown as a salad plant for its leaves. It adapts to any well-drained, loamy soil but needs full sun. Sow seeds in the spring when danger of frost is past, covering them with 6 mm ($\frac{1}{4}$ in.) of soil. Thin seedlings to stand 10 cm (4 in.) apart. Plants will bear fruit in about four months. To harvest, uproot the plants when the pods are brown and hang them upside down to dry in a warm, shady spot. Remove the dried seeds from the pods and store them in an airtight container. They are usually lightly roasted and then ground before being added as a spice to meat dishes.

COMMON THYME
Thymus vulgaris

FENUGREEK
Trigonella foenum-graecum

NASTURTIUM
Tropaeolum majus

COLTSFOOT
Tussilago farfara

TROPAEOLUM

T. majus (nasturtium, Indian cress)

Nasturtium is a climbing or trailing annual cultivated mainly for its ornamental qualities, but sometimes also for its spicy, peppery-tasting leaves, seeds and flowers. The leaves are eaten like watercress in sandwiches and salads, the flowers are used as a garnish for salads or to flavour vinegars, the pickled buds and seeds as a substitute for capers. The large, round, smooth-surfaced leaves, 5 to 17.5 cm (2 to 7 in.) in diameter, have long, soft stems. Climbing nasturtiums curl around any object they contact, holding the plant as it grows, sometimes as high as 1.8 to 3 metres (6 to 10 ft). Dwarf nasturtiums grow only 30 to 38 cm (1 to 1¼ ft) tall or less. Spurred flowers, 2.5 to 6 cm (1 to 2½ in.) wide, blossom in many colours—orange, yellow, creamy-white, scarlet, salmon, cerise and mahogany. They bloom continuously from early summer onwards until they are cut down by frost. The flowers are followed by clusters of seeds.

HOW TO GROW. Nasturtium, which is fully hardy throughout Europe, needs full sun and thrives in practically any soil. However, rich, moist soil encourages more leaf growth, a poor well-drained soil more flowers and seeds. Nasturtium seeds germinate in about two weeks, but they can be speeded by soaking in lukewarm water overnight before planting. Sow seeds outdoors in early spring after the danger of frost is past, covering them with 2 to 2.5 cm (¾ to 1 in.) of soil. Or start them in peat pots in a cold frame or on a window sill to be transplanted outdoors. When the seedlings are 5 to 7.5 cm (2 to 3 in.) high, thin or transplant them to stand about 15 cm (6 in.) apart for dwarf cultivars, 30 cm (1 ft) apart for climbing types. Nasturtiums attract aphids; if the leaves are to be harvested for salads, avoid chemical sprays and wash the insect pests away with a garden hose. Leaves may be cut at any time after the plants flower. Seeds should be gathered when they are still green and may be pickled in various ways. The simplest way is to place them in a bottle and cover them with a strongly flavoured vinegar.

Nasturtiums do well indoors provided they have at least four hours of direct sunlight a day, and temperatures that range from 4° to 7°C (40° to 45°F) at night to no more than 20°C (68°F) during the day. Sow three seeds in a 10 to 15 cm (4 to 6 in.) pot filled with a proprietary potting compost and cover them with a thin layer of soil. Keep the soil barely moist. If plants are grown for their leaves, fertilize every two weeks with a liquid fertilizer used at half the recommended strength. For plants grown for their flowers, feed monthly.

TUSSILAGO

T. farfara (coltsfoot, foalfoot, coughwort)

Coltsfoot is a curious plant whose flowers bloom and wither long before the first leaves appear. It is a hardy perennial that grows wild throughout Europe by rivers and inland waters, usually in clay soil. It has been associated with lung ailments since ancient times; even Pliny recommended the inhalation of the burnt roots. Herbalists since then have used the leaves for syrups and herbal brews to combat coughs, and sometimes recommend the dried leaves as a herbal tobacco. In country districts, home-made wine is made from the flowers. In France, a coltsfoot is a traditional sign over chemists' shops. In late winter and early spring, the plant produces flat, yellow, daisy-like flowers about 2.5 cm (1 in.) across that open on sunny days and ripen into tufted balls that disperse their seeds on the wind. The stems are thick and scaly and grow 7.5 to 15 cm (3 to 6 in.) tall; the leaves that follow the flowers have soft, downy undersides and are shaped like hoofprints.

HOW TO GROW. Coltsfoot thrives in full sun and adapts to almost any soil condition. It should be introduced in the garden with caution since it has creeping roots, spreads rapidly, and can be difficult to eradicate. Coltsfoot can be grown from seed or root cuttings planted in the early spring or autumn. When seedlings are 5 to 7.5 cm (2 to 3 in.) high, thin them to stand 20 cm (8 in.) apart. To get the sturdiest plants, divide the roots every three to four years and replant them in enriched soil.

U

ULMARIA See *Filipendula*

V

VALERIANA
V. officinalis (valerian, phew plant)

Valerian, a hardy perennial, was once grown for its strong smelling, carrot-shaped root, which attracts animals, especially rats, and according to legend was the secret ingredient carried by the Pied Piper of Hamelin. From the root's smell comes one of valerian's common names, phew plant. The scent of valerian is distasteful to some people, but in the Middle Ages it was used as a spice and to scent linen cupboards. The roots were dried and used for tonics and teas, said to be sleep-inducing.

Valerian is often included in perennial borders. It grows 1 to 1.5 metres (3 to 5 ft) tall, producing a clump of feathery foliage, 25 cm (10 in.) wide from which rise hollow flower stems bearing flat-topped clusters of fragrant, tiny, pink flowers that smell like heliotrope. The flowers, which blossom in early summer, often do not appear on seedlings until the second year of growth when the plants mature.

HOW TO GROW. Valerian is hardy in all parts of Europe and does well in full sun or partial shade. Although it grows best in rich, moist soil supplemented with garden compost, it tolerates almost any soil. Valerian can be started from seeds sown in spring or autumn. Do not cover the seeds—simply press them into damp soil. Most gardeners buy their first plants, then propagate by division of the roots. Space plants in the garden 38 to 45 cm ($1\frac{1}{4}$ to $1\frac{1}{2}$ ft) apart. After the flowers bloom, cut off the seed heads to keep plants from seeding themselves and to encourage root growth. After three years of flowering, valerian should be dug up, divided and replanted in enriched soil.

VALERIANELLA
V. locusta, also called *V. olitoria* (corn salad, lamb's lettuce)

Corn salad deserves wider recognition because it is ideal for an autumn and winter crop when other salad greens are scarce. It is easy to grow, and edible leaves are produced within a few weeks of sowing. It takes up less room than lettuce and can be tucked away in an out-of-the-way corner of the vegetable or herb garden. Corn salad is an annual, growing 15 to 30 cm (6 to 12 in.) high, with leaves 2.5 to 7.5 cm (1 to 3 in.) long. Tiny, inconspicuous, mauve flowers appear in early summer; these should be removed unless you want seed.

HOW TO GROW. Corn salad is fully hardy and grows extremely well in temperate and northern Europe. It does best in rich soil with plenty of organic matter, such as leaf-mould or well-rotted garden compost, and in full sun. Autumn-sown crops are better in a sheltered position. For a year-round supply of fresh leaves, make the first sowing in early spring and continue until early autumn. Sow the

VALERIAN
Valeriana officinalis

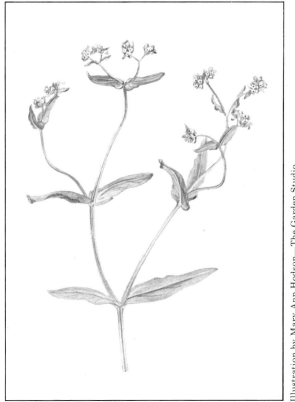

CORN SALAD
Valerianella locusta

Illustration by Mary Ann Hodson—The Garden Studio

GREAT MULLEIN
Verbascum thapsus

VERVAIN
Verbena officinalis

Illustration by Mary Ann Hodson—The Garden Studio

seeds in rows, 12 ṁm (½ in.) deep, and later thin the seed-lings to stand 15 cm (6 in.) apart. Apart from watering during prolonged dry weather and removing weeds, corn salad needs little attention. Begin harvesting the plants when they have produced four pairs of leaves; pull up and use whole plants or pick the largest leaves from each.

VERBASCUM
V. thapsus (great mullein, Aaron's rod, Jacob's staff, Our Lady's candle)

A majestic biennial herb, great mullein grows 1 to 1.8 mètres (3 to 6 ft) tall and is valued in the garden as a stately background plant. Since ancient times, the leaves and flowers have been used for dyes, herbal teas and remedies to relieve coughs and other chest complaints, and dressings for wounds; and the entire plant has been coated with suet and used as a candle.

In the first year of growth, large, woolly, 15 to 45 cm (½ to 1½ ft) long leaves spread out in a wide rosette at ground level, forming a grey-green ground cover that lasts through the winter; the leaves are covered on both sides with long, downy hairs. In the second year, stout spires of 2 to 2.5 cm (¾ to 1 in.) wide, yellow blossoms with pro-truding orange stamens rise above the ground foliage from late spring into midsummer. Their rigid, erect appearance inspired the popular names Aaron's rod and Jacob's staff. Great mullein's flowers attract bees and they can be used for dried flower arrangements.

HOW TO GROW. Great mullein is hardy in temperate and southern Europe, less so in cold northern regions. It needs full sun and a site sheltered from strong winds; it tolerates poor soil but does best in well-drained alkaline soil; in northern areas, where the soil freezes in the winter, good drainage is essential. Seeds must be sown in the late summer or early autumn where plants are to remain because the rosette clumps cannot be transplanted success-fully. Thin the seedlings to stand 60 cm (2 ft) apart.

VERBENA
V. officinalis (vervain)

Vervain is a wild plant, native to Britain, now almost neglected, but in former times it was surrounded by super-stitions. It was used by the ancient Druids in their religious rites, as offerings to their gods, and to perfume their holy stones, hence the common French name, *herbe sacrée*. Vervain was used in sorcery and witchcraft, as a love potion and in medicine. The leaves can be steeped for herbal teas which are said to counteract fevers and kidney troubles; some medieval herbalists recommended vervain tea against the plague, but John Gerard in his *Herball* (1597) discounted this as a falsehood.

Vervain is a perennial, growing 30 to 60 cm (1 to 2 ft) high, with upright stems sparsely clothed with mid-green, deeply cut leaves that are pleasantly aromatic. Tiny, bluish-purple flowers appear in slender branching spikes at the tops of the plants in summer. It is less attractive for garden decoration than the many cultivars of the related *Verbena* x *hybrida*.

HOW TO GROW. Vervain is hardy throughout Europe where it grows as a weed. It thrives in any, even poor soil and in full sun or light shade. New plants are raised from seed sown in the open where the plants are to flower, or from root division in early spring; space them 38 cm (1¼ ft) apart.

VERBENA TRIPHYLLA See *Lippia*

VERONICA
V. officinalis (speedwell)

The creeping stems and delicate, pale blue blossoms of speedwell have made it a popular ground cover. This tiny perennial has prostrate, hairy branches, 5 to 45 cm (2 to 18 in.) long with oval, tooth-edged leaves 6 to 25 mm ($\frac{1}{4}$ to 1 in.) long. Its flowering stalks, 2.5 to 6 cm (1 to $2\frac{1}{2}$ in.) long, jut upwards at the junction of leaf and stem throughout summer. The leaves can be used for herbal teas.

HOW TO GROW. Speedwell grows in all parts of Europe. It does best in dry, well-drained soils and thrives in full sun, but will grow in partial shade. It grows wild on heathland in many parts of Europe. Start plants from seed, stem cuttings or root divisions in the spring, spacing plants or thinning seedlings to stand about 30 cm (1 ft) apart. Nip off faded blossoms to encourage new flowers and additional growth. Divide root clumps every three or four years in the spring or autumn to prevent overcrowding. A large number of cultivated creeping speedwell species and cultivars are readily available from nurseries and seedsmen.

VIOLA
V. odorata (sweet violet, florist's violet); *V. tricolor* (heartsease, wild pansy)

Although they belong to the same genus, the sweet violet and heartsease are admired for different reasons. Sweet violet is one of the most fragrant of flowers. Its scent is an ingredient of perfumes and potpourris. The flower itself is candied for use as a confection or cake decoration. It is also infused and used as flavouring in creams, ices and liqueurs, and is sometimes, as in the Middle Ages, added to salads for unusual colour and flavour. Heartsease is cultivated for its bright tricoloured flowers, which bloom profusely in spring and summer. The flowers were once used in concoctions for chest complaints, hence the most well known of its many names.

Sweet violet is a perennial with creeping roots; it grows 15 to 20 cm (6 to 8 in.) high and produces heart-shaped crinkly leaves, 6 cm ($2\frac{1}{2}$ in.) across. Deep violet, pink or white flowers, 2 cm ($\frac{3}{4}$ in.) across, bloom from mid to late spring. Heartsease is a biennial that seeds itself each year and therefore, once planted, is a permanent element in the garden; in fact, it has great tenacity. The plant, 7.5 to 20 cm (3 to 8 in.) high, blooms from mid-spring through to late summer and, apart from its colourful 2 cm ($\frac{3}{4}$ in.) pansy-like flowers, is also notable for its leaves. On the single stem, spreading individual leaves can be heart-shaped, notched, lance-shaped or feathery.

HOW TO GROW. Both plants are native to Europe and grow wild and cultivated in all parts. Sweet violet thrives in any moderately rich, moist, well-drained soil supplemented with garden compost, manure or leaf-mould; it is a woodland plant and does best in partial shade. Heartsease is a meadow plant and thrives in bright sun; it grows in almost any soil and any site, from windswept dunes to rocky uplands.

Although sweet violet and heartsease can be started from seed sown 2 mm ($\frac{1}{8}$ in.) deep, neither will bloom until the second year. Set out plants in the early spring, placing heartsease 10 to 15 cm (4 to 6 in.) apart, sweet violets 25 to 30 cm (10 to 12 in.) apart. Keep the soil moist but not soggy until the plants are established. During the winter, protect them with a mulch of leaves. To propagate sweet violets, divide root clumps late in the spring after flowering or remove rooted runners in early spring. Harvest sweet violets when the flowers first open and their fragrance is strongest. Dry them in a shady, well-ventilated place and store them in an airtight container.

SPEEDWELL
Veronica officinalis

SWEET VIOLET
Viola odorata

HEARTSEASE
Viola tricolor

Characteristics of 127 herbs

	USES										PROPAGATION			PLANT TYPE			SOIL NEEDS		LIGHT NEEDS		HEIGHT			
	Culinary seasonings	Salad greens	Teas	Fragrances	Dried arrangements	Decorative foliage	Decorative flowers	Source of bee nectar	House plants	Seeds	Stem cuttings	Bulbs	Root divisions	Hardy perennial	Tender perennial	Annual or biennial	Dry	Wet to moist	Direct sunlight	Shade or partial shade	Under 30 cm (1 ft)	30 to 90 cm (1 to 3 ft)	90 to 150 cm (3 to 5 ft)	Over 150 cm (5 ft)
ACHILLEA MILLEFOLIUM (yarrow)				●				●				●	●	●			●		●		●			
ACORUS CALAMUS (sweet flag)				●								●	●	●				●	●			●	●	
AGASTACHE FOENICULUM (anise hyssop)			●				●	●				●	●	●			●	●	●			●	●	
AGRIMONIA EUPATORIA (agrimony)						●		●				●	●	●			●		●			●	●	
AJUGA REPTANS (bugle)						●							●	●				●	●	●	●			
ALCHEMILLA XANTHOCHLORA (lady's mantle)	●				●	●	●		●	●		●	●	●				●		●	●			
ALLIUM ASCALONICUM (shallot)		●								●		●	●					●	●		●			
ALLIUM CEPA var. VIVIPARUM (Egyptian onion)		●								●		●	●					●	●					
ALLIUM PORRUM (leek)	●	●								●			●			●		●	●					
ALLIUM SATIVUM (garlic)		●								●			●					●	●		●			
ALLIUM SCHOENOPRASUM (chive)	●									●			●					●	●	●				
ALOE BARBADENSIS (aloe)									●		●	●			●		●		●					
ALTHAEA OFFICINALIS (marsh mallow)					●					●	●			●		●		●	●					●
ANCHUSA OFFICINALIS (alkanet)	●									●	●			●				●	●		●			
ANETHUM GRAVEOLENS (dill)	●						●	●								●		●	●				●	
ANGELICA ARCHANGELICA (angelica)	●		●	●									●	●		●		●	●				●	●
ANTHEMIS NOBILIS (chamomile)			●	●							●			●			●		●	●	●			
ANTHRISCUS CEREFOLIUM (chervil)	●	●					●	●								●		●	●		●			
ARMORACIA RUSTICANA (horseradish)	●										●	●		●				●	●			●		
ARTEMISIA ABSINTHIUM (wormwood)				●						●			●					●	●			●	●	
ARTEMISIA DRACUNCULUS (tarragon)	●						●	●			●	●						●	●			●		
ATRIPLEX HORTENSIS (sea purslane)		●			●					●						●		●	●					●
BORAGO OFFICINALIS (borage)	●	●					●			●			●	●				●	●					
BUXUS SEMPERVIRENS (common box)					●			●		●			●					●	●					●
CALENDULA OFFICINALIS (calendula)						●	●			●						●		●	●		●			
CALTHA PALUSTRIS (marsh marigold)						●	●			●	●	●						●	●		●			
CARDAMINE PRATENSIS (lady's smock)		●					●			●	●	●						●	●	●				
CARTHAMUS TINCTORIUS (safflower)	●				●		●			●				●	●			●	●		●			
CARUM CARVI (caraway)	●	●								●				●				●	●		●			
CHENOPODIUM ALBUM (fat hen)		●								●				●				●	●		●			
CHENOPODIUM BONUS-HENRICUS (Good King Henry)		●								●				●				●	●	●	●			
CHRYSANTHEMUM BALSAMITA (costmary)		●		●						●	●							●	●		●			
CHRYSANTHEMUM PARTHENIUM (feverfew)				●	●	●	●			●				●				●	●		●			
CICHORIUM INTYBUS (chicory)	●		●				●			●				●				●	●			●		
CITRUS MICROCARPA (calamondin orange)			●			●		●	●	●	●		●			●		●	●		●			
CORIANDRUM SATIVUM (coriander)	●									●						●		●	●		●			
CRITHMUM MARITIMUM (samphire)	●	●								●	●	●		●				●	●	●				
CROCUS SATIVUS (saffron crocus)	●						●					●		●			●		●		●			
CUMINUM CYMINUM (cumin)	●									●					●	●		●	●		●			
CYNARA CARDUNCULUS (cardoon)		●					●			●				●	●		●	●				●		
CYTISUS SCOPARIUS (broom)		●					●			●	●			●			●		●					●
DICTAMNUS ALBUS (gas plant)			●		●	●	●			●				●			●		●		●			
DIPSACUS SYLVESTRIS (teasel)					●					●					●			●	●					●
FILIPENDULA VULGARIS (meadowsweet)			●	●						●				●				●	●		●			
FOENICULUM VULGARE (fennel)	●			●						●		●	●					●	●				●	
FOENICULUM VULGARE var. DULCE (Florence fennel)		●								●				●				●	●		●			
FRAGARIA VESCA (alpine strawberry)										●			●				●	●	●	●				
GALIUM ODORATUM (woodruff)	●		●			●			●	●	●	●						●		●	●			
GALIUM VERUM (lady's bedstraw)			●							●		●	●					●	●		●			
GLYCYRRHIZA GLABRA (liquorice)	●									●		●	●					●	●		●			

	USES									PROPAGATION				PLANT TYPE			SOIL NEEDS		LIGHT NEEDS		HEIGHT			
	Culinary seasonings	Salad greens	Teas	Fragrances	Dried arrangements	Decorative foliage	Decorative flowers	Source of bee nectar	House plants	Seeds	Stem cuttings	Bulbs	Root divisions	Hardy perennial	Tender perennial	Annual or biennial	Dry	Wet to moist	Direct sunlight	Shade or partial shade	Under 30 cm (1 ft)	30 to 90 cm (1 to 3 ft)	90 to 150 cm (3 to 5 ft)	Over 150 cm (5 ft)
HELIOTROPIUM ARBORESCENS (common heliotrope)				●						●					●			●	●	●				
HYSSOPUS OFFICINALIS (hyssop)	●		●				●	●		●					●			●	●			●		
INULA HELENIUM (elecampane)	●					●		●		●					●			●	●					●
IRIS GERMANICA var. FLORENTINA (orris)				●								●	●	●	●		●			●		●		
ISATIS TINCTORIA (woad)						●	●			●					●	●		●	●				●	
JASMINUM OFFICINALE (jasmine)				●			●	●	●	●	●				●			●	●					●
JUNIPERUS COMMUNIS (juniper)	●			●	●	●				●					●			●	●					●
LAMIUM MACULATUM (spotted dead nettle)	●					●	●			●					●			●		●	●			
LAURUS NOBILIS (sweet bay)				●		●			●	●					●		●			●				●
LAVANDULA ANGUSTIFOLIA (English lavender)				●			●	●		●	●			●			●		●			●		
LAVANDULA DENTATA (fringed lavender)				●			●	●	●	●	●				●			●	●			●		
LAVANDULA STOECHAS (French lavender)				●			●	●	●	●	●				●			●	●			●		
LEPIDIUM SATIVUM (garden cress)	●	●								●						●		●	●		●			
LEVISTICUM OFFICINALE (lovage)	●	●					●			●			●	●	●			●	●				●	●
LIPPIA CITRIODORA (lemon verbena)	●		●	●	●						●				●			●	●					●
MARRUBIUM VULGARE (horehound)			●	●			●			●					●		●		●			●		
MATRICARIA CHAMOMILLA (German chamomile)			●	●		●	●			●					●	●	●		●		●			
MELISSA OFFICINALIS (lemon balm)	●		●	●						●			●	●				●	●			●		
MENTHA X PIPERITA (peppermint)			●	●							●		●	●				●	●			●		
MENTHA PULEGIUM (pennyroyal)			●	●							●		●	●				●	●		●			
MENTHA ROTUNDIFOLIA (apple mint)			●	●		●	●				●		●	●				●	●			●		
MENTHA SPICATA (spearmint)	●	●	●	●							●		●	●				●	●			●		
MONARDA DIDYMA (bergamot)			●	●			●	●			●		●	●				●	●			●		
MYRRHIS ODORATA (sweet cicely)			●			●	●	●		●				●				●		●		●		
MYRTUS COMMUNIS (myrtle)	●			●		●	●			●					●			●	●				●	●
NASTURTIUM OFFICINALE (watercress)	●	●								●					●			●	●		●			
NEPETA CATARIA (catmint)			●	●		●	●	●		●			●	●				●	●			●		
OCIMUM BASILICUM (sweet basil)	●			●						●						●		●	●			●		
ORIGANUM DICTAMNUS (dittany of Crete)		●	●				●			●					●		●		●		●			
ORIGANUM MAJORANA (sweet marjoram)	●									●	●				●	●	●		●			●		
ORIGANUM ONITES (pot marjoram)	●									●					●		●		●			●		
ORIGANUM VULGARE (oregano)	●										●		●	●			●		●			●		
OSMANTHUS FRAGRANS (sweet olive)				●			●		●	●	●				●			●	●					●
PELARGONIUM X CITROSUM (lemon-scented geranium)				●					●	●	●	●			●		●		●			●		
PELARGONIUM X DOMESTICUM 'CLORINDA' (Clorinda geranium)				●		●			●	●	●	●			●		●		●			●		
PELARGONIUM GRAVEOLENS (rose-scented geranium)				●					●	●	●	●			●		●		●			●		
PELARGONIUM TOMENTOSUM (peppermint-scented geranium)				●		●	●		●		●				●		●		●			●		
PERILLA FRUTESCENS var. CRISPA (purple perilla)				●		●			●	●						●		●	●	●		●		
PETROSELINUM CRISPUM ssp. CRISPUM (parsley)	●									●						●		●	●		●			
PETROSELINUM CRISPUM ssp. TUBEROSUM (Hamburg parsley)	●									●						●		●	●			●		
PIMPINELLA ANISUM (anise)	●		●			●	●			●						●	●		●			●		
PORTULACA OLERACEA (purslane)		●				●				●						●	●		●		●			
PRIMULA VERIS (cowslip)							●			●			●					●	●	●	●			
ROSA DAMASCENA (damask rose)				●			●			●	●			●				●	●				●	
ROSA GALLICA (French rose)	●			●			●				●			●				●	●			●		
ROSMARINUS OFFICINALIS (rosemary)	●			●				●			●			●			●	●	●			●		
RUMEX SCUTATUS (sorrel)	●	●				●		●	●	●				●				●	●			●		
RUTA GRAVEOLENS (rue)	●			●	●	●	●			●				●				●	●	●				
SALVIA OFFICINALIS (sage)	●									●	●			●				●	●			●		
SALVIA SCLAREA (clary)	●		●				●		●	●	●					●	●	●				●		

151

	Culinary seasonings	Salad greens	Teas	Fragrances	Dried arrangements	Decorative foliage	Decorative flowers	Source of bee nectar	House plants	Seeds	Stem cuttings	Bulbs	Root divisions	Hardy perennial	Tender perennial	Annual or biennial	Dry	Wet to moist	Direct sunlight	Shade or partial shade	Under 30 cm (1 ft)	30 to 90 cm (1 to 3 ft)	90 to 150 cm (3 to 5 ft)	Over 150 cm (5 ft)
SANGUISORBA MINOR (burnet)	●	●	●		●	●		●	●				●					●	●		●			
SANTOLINA CHAMAECYPARISSUS (cotton lavender)			●		●		●	●					●					●	●		●			
SATUREJA HORTENSIS (summer savory)	●				●		●	●								●		●	●		●			
SATUREJA MONTANA (winter savory)	●				●		●	●		●		●		●				●	●			●		
SEMPERVIVUM TECTORUM (houseleek)						●	●	●					●	●				●	●		●			
SESAMUM INDICUM (sesame)	●					●			●				●					●						●
SINAPIS ALBA (white mustard)	●	●							●			●				●		●	●		●			
SIUM SISARUM (skirret)						●			●					●				●			●	●		
STACHYS OFFICINALIS (wood betony)			●		●				●				●	●				●	●		●			
STACHYS OLYMPICA (lamb's ears)						●			●				●	●				●	●		●			
SYMPHYTUM OFFICINALE (comfrey)						●	●		●				●					●	●	●		●		
TANACETUM VULGARE (tansy)	●			●	●	●			●				●	●				●	●		●			
TARAXACUM OFFICINALE (dandelion)		●					●		●					●		●		●	●		●			
TEUCRIUM CHAMAEDRYS (germander)						●	●		●				●	●				●	●		●			
THYMUS X CITRIODORUS (lemon thyme)	●		●	●		●	●	●	●		●		●	●				●	●		●			
THYMUS SERPYLLUM (wild thyme)	●		●	●		●	●	●	●		●		●	●				●	●		●			
THYMUS VULGARIS (common thyme)	●		●	●		●	●	●	●		●		●	●				●	●		●			
TRIGONELLA FOENUM-GRAECUM (fenugreek)	●		●			●			●							●		●	●		●			
TROPAEOLUM MAJUS (nasturtium)		●				●		●	●							●		●	●					●
TUSSILAGO FARFARA (coltsfoot)						●	●		●				●	●				●	●	●				
VALERIANA OFFICINALIS (valerian)			●			●			●				●	●				●	●	●			●	
VALERIANELLA LOCUSTA (corn salad)		●							●							●		●	●		●			
VERBASCUM THAPSUS (great mullein)					●	●	●	●	●					●		●	●	●	●				●	
VERBENA OFFICINALIS (vervain)			●	●					●				●			●		●	●		●			
VERONICA OFFICINALIS (speedwell)			●			●	●		●	●	●		●	●				●	●		●			
VIOLA ODORATA (sweet violet)			●			●			●			●	●					●		●	●			
VIOLA TRICOLOR (heartsease)						●	●		●							●		●	●	●	●			

Picture credits

The sources for the illustrations in this book are shown below. Credits from left to right are separated by semicolons, from top to bottom by dashes. Cover—Marina Schinz, courtesy Brooklyn Botanic Garden. 4—Courtesy of WGBH Educational Foundation; Sarah Tanner; Clem Harris, courtesy Frances Perry. 6—Derek Bayes, by permission of the Provost and Fellows of Eton College. 10, 11—Drawings by Matt Greene. 14, 15—Enrico Ferorelli. 18, 19—David Lees. 24—Fred De Van. 26 to 37—Drawings by Matt Greene. 41, 42, 43—Marina Schinz. 44—Fleming B. Fuller—Bob Waterman. 45—Fleming B. Fuller—John Perella. 46, 47—Enrico Ferorelli. 48, 49—Marina Schinz. 50—Enrico Ferorelli— Marina Schinz. 51—Marina Schinz—Enrico Ferorelli. 52, 53—Marina Schinz; Patrick Thurston. 54—Sonja Bullaty and Angelo Lomeo. 56, 58—Drawings by Matt Greene. 60 to 61—Ken Kay. 63, 64—Drawings by Matt Greene. 66—Peter Kaplan. 69 to 77—Drawings by Matt Greene. 79—Sonja Bullaty and Angelo Lomeo. 80—Marina Schinz; Sonja Bullaty and Angelo Lomeo—Al Satterwhite. 81—Sonja Bullaty and Angelo Lomeo. 82—Al Satterwhite; Sonja Bullaty and Angelo Lomeo. 83—Marina Schinz except bottom right Peter Kaplan. 88 to 149—Encyclopaedia illustrations by Richard Crist except where otherwise indicated next to illustration.

Acknowledgements

The editors would like to extend special thanks to Lizzie Boyd, Kingston-upon-Thames, Surrey. They also wish to thank the following: Jean Blackburn, American Association of Nurserymen, Washington, D.C.; Gavin Bridson, Linnean Society, London; Dr. Henry Cathey, U.S. Department of Agriculture, Washington, D.C.; Sergio Chiesa, Institute of Botany and Plant Physiology, University of Padua, Italy; Marie Therese Colonna, Falls Church, Va.; Mrs. David L. Conger, Stonington, Conn.; Bernard Currid, Brooklyn Botanic Garden, Brooklyn, N.Y.; Patrick Devlin, Keeper of

College Library and Collections, Eton College, Berkshire; Gertrude B. Foster, Falls Village, Conn.; Jane Opper Grace, New York City; Barbara Heinen, Horticultural Society of New York, New York City; The Herb Society of America, Boston, Mass.; Richard Holiman, Coventry, Conn.; Mrs. Frederic P. Houston, New York City; Mrs. Walter K. Howard, Wayne, Pa.; Dr. Peter Hyytio, L. H. Bailey Hortorium, Cornell University, Ithaca, N.Y.; Wallace Jackson, London; Dr. N. R. Ker, F.B.A., Edinburgh; Don Leaver, Bromley, Kent; Lornie Leete-Hodge, Devizes, Wiltshire; Giangiacomo Lorenzoni, Institute of Botany and Plant Physiology, University of Padua, Italy; The Marchioness of Salisbury, Cranborne Manor, Dorset; Judge Peter Mason, London; Polly Murray, McCormick and Co., Inc., Baltimore, Md.; Winona O'Connor, London; Giampaolo Porlezza, Como, Italy; Robin Price, Wellcome Institute for the History of Medicine, London; Mrs. J. Pancost Reath, Radnor, Pa.; Mrs. George A. Reed, Jr., Malvern, Pa.; Paolo Rovesti, President, Centro Italiano Per L'Erboristeria, Milan; John Sales, National Trust, London; Kay Sanecki, Tring, Hertfordshire; Elizabeth Scholtz, Director, Brooklyn Botanic Garden, Brooklyn, N.Y.; Diane Schwartz, The New York Botanical Garden, Bronx, N.Y.; Dr. Malcolm Stewart, Society of Herbalists, London; Milton Taylor, Manager, Caswell-Massey, Ltd., New York City; Gabrielle Townsend, London; Mrs. Charles S. Truitt, Haverford, Pa.; Rosemary Verey, Barnsley House, Gloucestershire; W. Williams, Department of Prints and Drawings, British Museum, London; Betty Wylder, Long Beach, Calif.

Bibliography

Bailey, L. H., *The Standard Clopedia of Horticulture* (3 vols.). Collier-Macmillan, 1935.

Brooklyn Botanic Garden, *Handbook on Herbs*. BBG, 1971.

Brooklyn Botanic Garden, *Herbs and Their Ornamental Uses*. BBG, 1972.

Campbell, Mary Mason, *Betty Crocker's Kitchen Gardens*. Western Publishing Co., Inc., 1971.

Chittenden, Fred J., *The Royal Horticultural Society Dictionary of Gardening*. Oxford University Press, 1956 and 1974.

Clarkson, Rosetta E., *The Golden Age of Herbs and Herbalists*. Dover Publications, Inc., 1973. (Reprint of *Green Enchantment*. Macmillan Company, Inc., 1940.)

Clarkson, Rosetta E., *Herbs: Their Culture and Uses*. Macmillan Publishing Company, Inc., 1942.

Culpeper, Nicholas, *The English Physician Enlarged*. Peter Cole, 1656.

Dioscorides, Pedanius, *Greek Herbal*. Ed. by Robert T. Gunther, translated by John Goodyear. Hafner Press, 1968. (Reprint of 1933 ed.)

Doole, Louise Evans, *Herbs for Health: How to Grow and Use Them*. Wilshire, 1972.

Elbert, Virginia F. and George A., *Fun with Growing Herbs Indoors*. Crown Publishers, Inc., 1974.

Foster, Gertrude B., *Herbs for Every Garden*. J. M. Dent, 1975.

Fox, Helen Morgenthau, *Gardening with Herbs for Flavor and Fragrance*. Dover Publications, 1933.

Graf, Alfred Byrd, *Exotica*. Roehrs Company Inc., 1957.

Grieve, Mrs. M., *A Modern Herbal* (2 vols.). Jonathan Cape, 1974.

Hall, Dorothy, *The Book of Herbs*. Angus and Robertson, 1973. Pan Books, 1976.

Herb Society of America, *Herbs for Use and for Delight*. Dover Publications, Inc., 1975.

Herb Society of America, *A Primer for Herb Growing*. HSA, 1966.

Herb Society of America, *Simple Rules for Herb Cookery*. HSA, 1954.

Hériteau, Jacqueline, *Herbs*. Grosset & Dunlap, Inc., 1975.

Hoffman, Irene Botsford, *The Book of Herb Cookery*. Gramercy Publishing Company, 1940.

Hylton, William H., and others, *The Rodale Herb Book*. Rodale Press Books, Inc., 1974.

Loewenfeld, Claire, and Back, Philippa, *The Complete Book of Herbs and Spices*. David and Charles, 1975.

Loewenfeld, Claire, and Back, Philippa, *Herbs, Health and Cookery*. Pan Books, 1971.

Mazza, Irma Goodrich, *Herbs for the Kitchen*. Little, Brown & Co., 1975.

Miloradovich, Milo, *Art of Cooking with Herbs and Spices*. Doubleday & Co., Inc., 1950.

Muenscher, Walter Conrad, and Rice, Myron Arthur, *Garden Spice and Wild Pot-Herbs*. Comstock Editions, Inc., 1955.

Northcote, Lady Rosalind, *The Book of Herb Lore*. Dover Publications, Inc., 1971.

Sanecki, Kay N., *The Complete Book of Herbs*. Macdonald, 1974.

Schafer, Violet, *Herbcraft*. Yerba Buena Press, 1971.

Simmons, Adelma G., *Herb Gardening in Five Seasons*. Hawthorn Books, Inc., 1964.

Simmons, Adelma G., *Herb Gardens of Delight*. Hawthorn Books, Inc., 1974.

Simmons, Adelma G., *Herbs to Grow Indoors*. Hawthorn Books, Inc., 1969.

Simmons, Adelma G., *A Merry Christmas Herbal*. William Morrow & Co., Inc., 1968.

Sunset Books, *Cooking with Spices and Herbs*. Lane Publishing Co., 1976.

Sunset Books, *How to Grow Herbs*. Lane Publishing Co., 1976.

Taylor, Norman, ed., *Encyclopedia of Gardening*. Houghton Mifflin Company, 1936.

Webster, Helen, *Herbs: How to Grow Them and How to Use Them*. Charles T. Branford Co., 1942.

Wyman, Donald, *Wyman's Gardening Encyclopedia*. Macmillan Publishing Company, Inc., 1971.

Zander, R., *Handwörterbuch der Pflanzennamen*. Verlag Eugen Ulmer, 1972.

Index

Numerals in italics indicate an illustration of the subject mentioned

A

Aaron's rod. *See Verbascum thapsus*
Absinthe, 23
Accelerator, compost, 29
Achillea, 90
Achillea filipendulina, *83*
Achillea millefolium, *90*
Acidity, 29
Aconite, 21
Acorus, 90
Acorus calamus, *90*
Agastache, 90
Agastache anethiodora, 90
Agastache foeniculum, *90*
Agrimonia, 91
Agrimonia eupatoria, *91*
Agrimony, *51*, *91*. *See also Agrimonia eupatoria*
Air, 64
Air fresheners, 21
Ajuga, 91
Ajuga reptans, *91*
Alchemilla, 91
Alchemilla vulgaris, 91
Alchemilla xanthochlora, 91, *92*
Alecost. *See Chrysanthemum and Tanacetum*
Algae, 59
Alkalinity, 29
Alkanet, 12, *95*. *See also Anchusa officinalis*
Allium, 92-94
Allium ascalonicum, *92*
Allium cepa var. *aggregatum*, *93*
Allium cepa var. *viviparum*, *92*, 93
Allium porrum, 92, *93*
Allium sativum, 92, *93*
Allium schoenoprasum, 92, *93*
Aloe, 23, 55, 62, *94*
Aloe barbadensis, *94*
Aloe, true. *See Aloe barbadensis*
Aloe vera, 94
Aloe vulgaris, 94
Aloysia. See Lippia
Alpine strawberry, *112*. *See also Fragaria vesca*
Althaea, 95
Althaea officinalis, *94*, 95
Aluminium sulphate, 29
Amaracus. See Origanum
Analysis, soil, 29
Anchusa, 95
Anchusa officinalis, *95*
Anethum, 96
Anethum graveolens, *96*
Angelica, 21, 22, 23, *47*, 56, *96*
Angelica archangelica, *96*
Anise, 13, 57, 84, *132*. *See also Pimpinella anisum*
Anise fern. *See Myrrhis odorata*
Anise, harvesting, 72
Anise hyssop, *90*. *See also Agastache foeniculum*
Anise seeds, 23
Anise seeds, harvesting, 76
Aniseed. *See Pimpinella anisum*
Anisum. See Pimpinella
Annual herbs, 9, 26, 31, 33
Annual herbs, disbudding, 39
Annual herbs, harvesting, 69
Annual herbs, propagation, 36
Anthemis, 97
Anthemis nobilis, *97*
Anthriscus, 98
Anthriscus cerefolium, *98*
Appearance, 11
Aphrodisiacs, 13
Apple mint, 11, 12, 30, *122*, *123*. *See also Mentha rotundifolia*
Armoracia, 98
Armoracia rusticana, *98*
Aromatic herbs, 16, 21
Aromatic oils, 10
Artemisia, 7, 10, *14-15*, *46*, *66*, *83*, 87, 89, 99
Artemisia absinthium, *99*
Artemisia camphorata, 86
Artemisia dracunculus, *99*
Artichoke, wild. *See Cynara cardunculus*
Artificial light, 63, *64*
Ashes, wood, 33
Asperula. See Galium
Associations, food, 76
Associations, plant, 27
Astrology, herbs in, 20
Atriplex, 100
Atriplex hortensis, *100*
Autumn division, *35*
Autumn feeding, 65
Autumn planting, 32
Autumn sowing, 34

B

Bachelor's buttons, 85
Bacteria, 29
Bag herbs, 77
Balm, 22. *See also Melissa officinalis*
Balm, bee, 12, 26, 84, 85. *See also Monarda didyma*
Balm, lemon, 8, 12, 85, *121*. *See also Melissa officinalis*
Balm, storing, 73
Balm, sweet. *See Melissa officinalis*
Barbados aloe. *See Aloe barbadensis*
Barberry, *48-49*
Bark mulch, 36
Basic herbs, 30
Basil, 7, 9, 12, 16, 27, 30, *51*, *52*, *54*, 55, 56, 57, 58, 76, 77, 78, 84, 85, 87, *88*. *See also Ocimum basilicum*
Basil, disbudding, 68
Basil, drying, 71
Basil, freezing, 73
Basil jelly, 78, *79*
Basil, pinching out, 39
Basil sauce, 84
Basil vinegar, 77, *80*, *81*
Baskets, hanging herb, 56
Bath fragrances, 16, 86, 87
Bay, drying, 71
Bay, indoor, 56
Bay laurel, 13. *See also Laurus nobilis*
Bay leaf. *See Laurus nobilis*
Bay, pests, 59
Bay, sweet, 11, 13, 55, *66*, 77, *117*. *See also Laurus nobilis*
Bay vinegar, 77
Bay, winter care, 39
Beds, herb, 26, 27
Beds, herbs for, 11
Beds, raised, *30*, *31*, 40, *44*, *45*
Bedstraw, 12
Bee balm, 12, 26, 84, 85. *See also Monarda didyma*
Bee bread. *See Borago officinalis*
Bee gardens, 12
Beefsteak plant. *See Perilla frutescens* var. *crispa*
Bees, honey, 12, *24*
Begonia, *48-49*
Bench cobbler's. *See Lamium maculatum*
Bergamot, *45*, *123*. *See also Monarda didyma*
Bergamot, propagation, 36, 38
Betony, woolly. *See Stachys olympica*
Betony, wood, *51*, *141*. *See also Stachys officinalis*
Bible leaf. *See Chrysanthemum balsamita*
Biennial herbs, 9
Biennial herbs, disbudding, 39
Bird's-foot. *See Trigonella foenum-graecum*
Bishop's wort. *See Stachys officinalis*
Bitter aloe. *See Aloe barbadensis*
Bitter buttons. *See Tanacetum vulgare*
Bitter-cress. *See Cardamine pratensis*
Bitter herbs, 99
Black sugar. *See Glycyrrhiza glabra*
Blackwort. *See Symphytum officinale*
Blanching, 75
Blossom, 40
Bonafede, Francesco, 18
Bone-meal, 33
Borage, 8, 9, 12, 21, 22, 67, 85, *100*. *See also Borago officinalis*
Borage, sowing, 34
Borage, storing, 73
Borago, 100
Borago officinalis, *100*
Borax, 86
Borders, herbs for, 11, 12, 25
Botanical names, 89
Bouquet garni, 13, 55, 76, 77, 130, 144
Bouquets, dried, 67, *82-83*
Box, common. 11. *48-49*. *101*. *See also Buxus sempervirens*
Bracken mulches, 39
Brassica. See Sinapis
Bread, bee. *See Borago officinalis*
Breeze-blocks, *45*
Brick edging, *11*, 31, 40, *44*, *51*
Bridal bouquets, *82*
Broom, *109*. *See also Cytisus scoparius*
Bugle, *91*. *See also Ajuga reptans*
Bugleweed. *See Ajuga reptans*
Bugloss. *See Anchusa officinalis*
Building blocks, 31
Burdock, 21
Burn, fertilizer, 65
Burnet, 9, 67, *83*, *137*. *See also Sanguisorba minor*
Burnet, freezing, 73
Burnet, harvesting, 68
Burnet, salad. *See Sanguisorba minor*
Burnet vinegar, *80*, *81*

Burning bush. *See Dictamnus albus*
Butters, herb, 67, 77
Buttons, bitter. *See Tanacetum vulgare*
Buxus, 101
Buxus sempervirens, *101*
Buying herbs, 33, 57

C

Cabbage, St. Patrick's. *See Sempervivum tectorum*
Calamondin orange, *106*. *See also Citrus microcarpa*
Calamus, 22. *See also Acorus*
Calendula. 12, 84, 85, *101*
Calendula officinalis, *101*
Caltha, 102
Caltha palustris, *102*
Caprilands tea, 84
Caraway, 13, 23, 36, 57, *103*. *See also Carum carvi*
Caraway, harvesting, 72
Caraway seeds, harvesting, 76
Cardamine, 102
Cardamine pratensis, *102*
Cardoon, *108*. *See also Cynara cardunculus*
Carthamus, 102
Carthamus tinctorius, *103*
Carum, 103
Carum carvi, *103*
Castile, rose of. *See Rosa damascena*
Catmint, 12, 84, *125*. *See also Nepeta cataria*
Catnip, 70. *See also Nepeta cataria*
Cat's peas. *See Cytisus scoparius*
Chaff, discarding, 72, 76
Chair, golden. *See Cytisus scoparius*
Chamomile, 12, 21, 22, *51*, 84, *97*. *See also Anthemis nobilis*
Chamomile, German, *121*. *See also Matricaria chamomilla*
Chamomile, Roman. *See Anthemis nobilis*
Chamomilla. See Matricaria
Chartreuse liqueur, 17
Cheese rennet. *See Galium odoratum*
Cheesecloth, 33, 34
Chemistry, soil, 29
Chenopodium, 104
Chenopodium album, *104*
Chenopodium bonus-henricus, *104*
Cherry pie. *See Heliotropium arborescens*
Chervil, 9, 27, 76, 77, *98*. *See also Anthriscus cerefolium*
Chervil, feeding, 36
Chervil, giant. *See Myrrhis odorata*
Chervil, harvesting, 69
Chicken wire, 58
Chicory, 9, *105*, 143. *See also Cichorium intybus*
Chinese parsley. *See Coriandrum sativum*
Chives, 7, 9, *24*, 27, 30, 58, 76, 78, *88*, *93*. *See also Allium schoenoprasum*
Chives, cutting, 68, *69*
Chives, disbudding, 39, 68
Chives, division, *35*
Chives, dried, 75
Chives, freezing, 73, 74
Chives, indoor, 56, 57
Chives, ornamental, *51*, *83*
Chives, potting, 37
Chives, propagation, 36
Chives, winter care, 39
Chrysanthemum, 104
Chrysanthemum balsamita, *104*
Chrysanthemum parthenium, 104, *105*
Chrysanthemum vulgare. See Tanacetum
Church steeples. *See Agrimonia eupatoria*
Cicely, sweet, 9, *124*. *See also Myrrhis odorata*
Cichorium, 105
Cichorium intybus, *105*
Cinquefoil, 16
Cinquefoil, Nepal, *44*
Citrus, 106
Citrus microcarpa, *106*
Citrus mitis, 106
Clary, *137*. *See also Salvia sclarea*
Clay pots, 59
Clay soils, 28
Clorinda geranium, 60, *129*. *See also Pelargonium* x *domesticum*
Coastal herb gardens, 50
Cobbler's bench. *See Lamium maculatum*
Cochlearia. See Armoracia
Cocklebur. *See Agrimonia eupatoria*
Colchicum autumnale, 107
Coleus, summer. *See Perilla frutescens* var. *crispa*
Cologne water, 17
Colour, 12, 40
Colour contrasts, 10
Coltsfoot, *146*. *See also Tussilago farfara*
Comfrey, 22, 87, *142*. *See also Symphytum officinale*
Common box, 11, *48-49*, *101*. *See also Buxus*

sempervirens
Common heliotrope. See *Heliotropium arborescens*
Common jasmine. See *Jasminum officinale*
Compost, 28, 30, 32, 33, 35, 36, 89
Compost accelerator, 29
Compost heap, 29
Compost, potting, 56, 58, 62, 89
Condensation, 73
Container-grown plants, 9
Containers, herb, 58, 59
Containers, potpourri, 86
Containers, storage, 73
Contrasts, colour, 10, 12, 14-15
Contrasts, textures, 10
Coriander, 27, 57, 106. See also *Coriandrum sativum*
Coriander, harvesting, 72
Coriander seeds, harvesting, 76
Coriander, storing, 73
Coriandrum, 106
Coriandrum sativum, 106
Corn salad, 147. See also *Valerianella locusta*
Cosmetics, herbs for, 23
Costmary, 104. See also *Chrysanthemum balsamita*
Cotton lavender, 12, 31, 42, 45, 83, 86, 138. See also *Santolina chamaecyparissus*
Coughwort. See *Tussilago farfara*
Cowslip, 133. See also *Primula veris*
Cranborne Manor, 52-53
Creeping thyme. See *Thymus serpyllum*
Crème de menthe, 23
Creosote, 30, 31
Cress, garden, 9, 16, 119. See also *Lepidium sativum*
Cress, Indian. See *Tropaeolum majus*
Cress, pepper. See *Lepidium sativum*
Crithmum, 107
Crithmum maritimum, 107
Crocks, 62, 63
Crocus, 107
Crocus sativus, 107
Crocus, saffron, 16, 107. See also *Crocus sativus*
Cuckoo flower. See *Cardamine pratensis*
Culinary herbs, 7, 8, 17, 23, 46, 55, 67
Culpeper, Nicholas, 20, 130
Cumin, 13, 67, 108. See also *Cuminum cyminum*
Cumin, harvesting, 72
Cuminum, 108
Cuminum cyminum, 108
Cuminum odorum, 108
Curdwort. See *Galium odoratum*
Cutting herbs, 68, 72
Cuttings, 57
Cuttings, root, 38
Cuttings, stem, 9, 37, 38
Cuttings, tip, 37, 38
Cuttings, transplanting, 37, 38
Cynara, 108
Cynara cardunculus, 108
Cytisus, 109
Cytisus scoparius, 109

D

Damask rose, 133. See also *Rosa damascena*
Dandelion, 9, 21, 70, 143. See also *Taraxacum officinale*
Dead nettle, spotted, 117. See also *Lamium maculatum*
Decongestants, 13
Decorative herbs, 40-53
Delphinium, 51, 85
Deodorizers, 13
Depth, sowing, 33
Designs, herb gardens, 10-11, 26-27, 40-53
Dessert flavourings, 84
Diazinon, 59
Dictamnus, 109
Dictamnus albus, 109
Dictamnus fraxinella, 109
Digitalis, 23
Dill, 9, 13, 26, 27, 30, 36, 54, 57, 78, 83, 88, 96. See also *Anethum graveolens*
Dill, feeding, 36
Dill, freezing, 73
Dill, harvesting, 72
Dill seeds, harvesting, 76
Dill, sowing, 34
Dill vinegar, 80, 81
Dioscorides, 16
Dips, 78
Dipsacus, 110
Dipsacus fullonum, 110
Dipsacus sylvestris, 110
Disbudding, 39, 68
Discoloration, leaf, 59
Disease repellants, 23
Disease resistance, 8, 36
Displaying herbs, 41-53
Distances, planting, 10, 26

Dittany of Crete, 12, 127. See also *Origanum dictamnus*
Dittany, false. See *Dictamnus albus*
Division, 35, 36
Doctrine of Signatures, 20
Donkey's ears. See *Stachys olympica*
Drainage, 25, 26, 28, 29, 40, 55, 62
Drainage holes, 62
Dressings, salad, 78
Dried arrangements, 7, 8, 67, 82-83
Dried herbs, 8, 10
Drink flavourings, 67, 84
Dropwort. See *Filipendula vulgaris*
Drugs, synthetic, 13, 22, 23
Drying herbs, 68, 70, 72, 85
Drying trays, 71, 74
Dwarf herbs, 10
Dyer's-weed. See *Isatis tinctoria*
Dyes, vegetable, 12, 22, 44, 67

E

Ears, donkey's. See *Stachys olympica*
Ears, lamb's, 142. See also *Stachys olympica*
Eau-de-Cologne, 17
Edging, 11, 31, 40, 44, 50, 51
Egyptian onion, 10, 92. See also *Allium cepa* var. *viviparum*
Elecampane, 22, 114. See also *Inula helenium*
Elizabethan knot gardens, 7, 10-11
English lavender. See *Lavandula angustifolia*
English names, 89
English Physician, The, 20
Ephedra, 13
Estragon. See *Artemisia dracunculus*
Eucalyptus seeds, 66
Evaporation, 65
Evergreen herbs, winter care, 39
Eyebright, 21

F

False dittany. See *Dictamnus albus*
False saffron. See *Carthamus tinctorius*
Fan palm, 18, 19
Farmyard manure, 28
Fat hen. See *Chenopodium album*
Feeding, 36, 65, 89
Fennel, 13, 26, 90, 111. See also *Foeniculum*
Fennel, feeding, 36
Fennel, Florence, 111. See also *Foeniculum vulgare* var. *dulce*
Fennel, freezing, 73
Fennel, hyssop. See *Agastache foeniculum*
Fennel, sea. See *Crithmum maritimum*
Fennel, sowing, 34
Fenugreek, 145. See also *Trigonella foenum-graecum*
Fern, anise. See *Myrrhis odorata*
Fertilizer burn, 65
Fertilizer salts, 59
Fertilizers, 28, 29, 30, 33, 35, 36, 65, 89
Feverfew, 105. See *Chrysanthemum parthenium*
Filipendula, 110
Filipendula hexapetala, 110
Filipendula vulgaris, 110
Fines herbes, 76, 77, 98, 99
Finocchio. See *Foeniculum*
Fixatives for potpourris, 86
Flag iris. See *Iris germanica* var. *florentina*
Flag, sweet, 21, 26, 90, See also *Acorus calamus*
Flavours, herb, 7, 13, 22
Flavours, herbs, dried and frozen, 75
Flavours, volume, 70
Florence fennel. See *Foeniculum vulgare* var. *dulce*
Florentine iris. See *Iris germanica* var. *florentina*
Florist's violet. See *Viola odorata*
Flower arrangements, dried, 7, 8, 67, 82-83
Flower buds, pinching out, 39
Flower pots, 59
Flowers, drying, 85, 86
Flowers, language of, 21
Fluorescent tubes, 64
Foalfoot. See *Tussilago farfara*
Focal points, 12, 40
Foeniculum, 111
Foeniculum dulce, 111
Foeniculum officinale, 111
Foeniculum vulgare, 90, 111
Foeniculum vulgare var. *dulce*, 111
Foliage, 40
Foliage colours, 12
Folk medicines, 22
Food associations, 76
Foxglove, 23, 45
Fragaria, 111
Fragaria vesca, 111, 112
Fragrance, 7, 8, 10, 11, 16, 17, 23, 25, 28, 31, 55, 84, 85
Fragrant herbs, 45, 46, 60-61

Fraxinella, 21. See also *Dictamnus albus*
Freezing herbs, 68, 73
French lavender, 118. See also *Lavandula stoechas*
French rose, 134. See also *Rosa gallica*
French spinach. See *Atriplex hortensis*
French tarragon, 9. See also *Artemisia dracunculus*
Fringed lavender, 118. See also *Lavendula dentata*
Frozen herbs, 8
Funeral herbs, 17, 22

G

Galium, 112-113
Galium odoratum, 112
Galium verum, 112, 113
Garden cress, 9, 119. See also *Lepidium sativum*
Garden sage. See *Salvia officinalis*
Garden of Simples, 18-19
Garden thyme. See *Thymus vulgaris*
Garlands, ceremonial, 13, 17
Garlic, 9, 13, 16, 21, 75, 93. See also *Allium sativum*
Garlic butter, 78
Garlic flowers, 83
Garlic vinegar, 77
Garnishes, 22, 74
Gas plant, 109. See also *Dictamnus albus*
Genus, 89
Geometric designs, 10-11, 27, 40, 41, 44, 45
Geranium. See *Pelargonium*
Geranium, peppermint, 54, 55, 61
Geranium, rose, 84, 85
Geraniums, scented, 8, 11, 60-61, 66, 78
Gerard, John, 20, 104
German chamomile, 121. See also *Matricaria chamomilla*
Germander, 7, 10, 12, 31, 44, 45, 143. See also *Teucrium chamaedrys*
Germander, wall. See *Teucrium chamaedrys*
Germination, 34
Giant chervil. See *Myrrhis odorata*
Glycyrrhiza, 113
Glycyrrhiza glabra, 113
Golden chair. See *Cytisus scoparius*
Golden rod, 21
Good King Henry, 104. See also *Chenopodium bonus-henricus*
Gooseberry geranium, 60
Goosefoot design, 27
Grace, herb of. See *Ruta graveolens*
Grappa, 136
Grass paths, 51
Great mullein, 148. See also *Verbascum thapsus*
Greek hayseed. See *Trigonella foenum-graecum*
Grete Herball, The, 17
Grey gardens, 12, 14-15
Ground-cover herbs, 11, 25, 50
Growth habits, 40
Gum benzoin, 86

H

Hamburg parsley. See *Petroselinum crispum* ssp. *tuberosum*
Hanging herb baskets, 56
Hardiness, 11, 89
Hard pan, 29
Harvesting herbs, 6, 66-87
Harvesting seeds, 72
Hayseed, Greek. See *Trigonella foenum-graecum*
Heap, compost, 29
Heartsease, 21, 149. See also *Viola tricolor*
Heather, 83
Hedges, 11, 17, 40, 42, 50
Hedges, lavender, 7, 11
Heights, 26
Heliotrope, common, 113. See also *Heliotropium arborescens*
Heliotropium, 113
Heliotropium arborescens, 113
Heliotropium corymbosum, 113
Heliotropium peruvianum, 113
Hen-and-chickens. See *Sempervivum tectorum*
Hen, fat. See *Chenopodium album*
Henbane, 19
Herb baskets, hanging, 56
Herb butters, 67, 77
Herb containers, 58
Herb, definition, 8
Herb displays, 41-53
Herb farms, 22
Herb gardens, 18-19
Herb gardens, coastal, 50

Herb gardens, miniature, *28*
Herb gardens, monastery, 12, 17
Herb gardens, sites for, 11, 25
Herb of grace. *See Ruta graveolens*
Herb harvests, 66-87
Herb jams, 78
Herb jellies, 78, *79*, 84
Herb mixtures, dried, 75
Herb pillows, 85, 86
Herb soaps, 87
Herb teas, 12, 13, 22, 70, 84
Herb vinegars, 67, 77, *80-81*
Herbal teas, 12, 13, 22, 70, 84
Herbalists, 16, 17, 22
Herball, 17, 20
Herbals, 17, 20
Herbs, annual, 9, 26, 31, 33
Herbs, biennial, 9
Herbs, bitter, 99
Herbs, decorative, 40-53
Herbs, dried, 8, 10
Herbs, drying, 68, 70, *72*, 85
Herbs, fragrant, 45, 46
Herbs, freezing, 68, 73
Herbs from seeds, 33
Herbs, frozen, 8
Herbs, growing conditions, 25
Herbs, harvesting, *6*, 66-87
Herbs, medicinal, 13
Herbs, perennial, 10
Herbs, pressed, 82, *83*
Herbs, salting, 74
Herbs, scented, 10
Herbs, spraying, 36
Herbs, storing, 73
Herbs, strewing, 16, 17, 21, 22
Herbs, window-sill, 54-65
Hessian, 33
Hippocrates, 16
Holes, drainage, 62
Holes, planting, *35*, 36, *58*
Honey bees, 12, *24*
Hop marjoram. *See Origanum dictamnus*
Horehound, 16, 22, *45*, 52, *120*. *See also Marubium vulgare*
Horehound, propagation, 38
Hormone rooting powder, 37, 38, 39
Horseheal. *See Inula helenium*
Horseradish, *19*, 26, 31, *46*, 57, *98*. *See also Armoracia rustica*
Houseleek, 62, *139*. *See also Sempervivum tectorum*
Humidifiers, 64
Humidity, 55, 64
Hungary water, 17
Hyssop, 10, *19*, 22, 27, *48-49*, 52, *114*. *See also Hyssopus officinalis*
Hyssop, anise, *90*. *See also Agastache foeniculum*
Hyssop, cutting down, 39
Hyssop, fennel. *See Agastache foeniculum*
Hyssop, sowing, 34
Hyssopus, 114
Hyssopus officinalis, *114*

I

Improving drainage, 29, 30
Incense, 16
Indian cress. *See Tropaeolum majus*
Indoor herbs, 7, 8, 54-65
Indoor herbs, potting, 37
Indoor propagation, 57
Indoor sowing, 34
Infusions, herb, 84
Insecticides, 36, 59
Insect infestations, 57, 59
Insect repellants, 22
Insects, removing, 59
Insects, scale, 59
Interior hedges, 11
Inula, 114
Inula helenium, *114*
Iris, 114
Iris, flag. *See Iris germanica var. florentina*
Iris, Florentine. *See Iris germanica var. florentina*
Iris germanica var. florentina, 114, *115*
Iron sulphate, 29
Isatis, 115
Isatis tinctoria, *115*
Ivy, 16

J

Jacob's staff. *See Verbascum thapsus*
Jams, herb, 78
Jars, 73
Jasmine, 55, *116*. *See also Jasminum officinale*
Jasmine, compost for, 62
Jasmine, propagation, 38
Jasmine, tea. *See Jasminum officinale*

Jasmine, white. *See Jasminum officinale*
Jasminum, 115
Jasminum officinale, 115, *116*
Jellies, herb, 78, *79*, 84
Juice, Spanish. *See Glycyrrhiza glabra*
Juniper, *15*, *116*. *See also Juniperus communis*
Juniperus, 116
Juniperus communis, *116*

K

Kingcup. *See Caltha palustris*
Kissing balls, 87
Kits, soil-testing, 29
Knit-bone. *See Symphytum officinale*
Knot gardens, 12, 40, *41*
Knot gardens, Elizabethan, 7, *10-11*
Knotted marjoram. *See Origanum majorana*
Kümmel, 23

L

Labelling, 69, 72, 73
Labels, plant, *32*, 34
Lady's bedstraw, *113*. *See also Galium verum*
Lady's mantle, *44*, *48-49*, *83*, *92*. *See also Alchemilla xanthochlora*
Lady's slipper. *See Cytisus scoparius*
Lady's smock, *102*. *See also Cardamine pratensis*
Lamb's ears, 12, *14-15*, *48-49*, *83*, *142*. *See also Stachys olympica*
Lamb's lettuce. *See Valerianella locusta*
Lamium, 117
Lamium maculatum, 117
Language of Flowers, 21
Latin names, 89
Laurel, 13
Laurel, bay. *See Laurus nobilis*
Laurus, 117
Laurus nobilis, 13, *117*
Lavandula, 118
Lavandula angustifolia, 118
Lavandula dentata, 118
Lavandula officinalis, 118
Lavandula spica, 118
Lavandula stoechas, 118
Lavandula vera, 118
Lavender, 7, 8, 10, 11, 12, *14*, 16, 17, 21, 23, *44*, *45*, *46*, *47*, *48-49*, *50*, 57, 85, 86, 118. *See also Lavandula*
Lavender, cotton, *138*. *See also Santolina chamaecyparissus*
Lavender, English. *See Lavandula angustifolia*
Lavender, French, *118*. *See also Lavandula stoechas*
Lavender, fringed, *118*. *See also Lavandula dentata*
Lavender, propagation, 37
Lavender, true. *See Lavandula angustifolia*
Layering, 38, 57
Layouts, herb beds, 26-27
Leaf discoloration, 59
Leaves, harvesting, 62, *72*
Leaves, seed, *32*
Leek, 10, *93*. *See also Allium porrum*
Lemon balm, 8, 12, 85, *121*. *See also Melissa officinalis*
Lemon balm, potting up, 57
Lemon balm, propagation, 37
Lemon-scented geranium, *128*. *See also Pelargonium x citrosum*
Lemon thyme, 10, *44*, *144*. *See also Thymus x citriodorus*
Lemon verbena, 11, 12, 84, 85, *120*. *See also Lippia citriodora*
Lemon verbena, drying, 71
Lemon verbena, indoor, 56
Leontodon. See Taraxacum
Lepidium, 119
Lepidium sativum, 119
Lettuce, lamb's. *See Valerianella locusta*
Levisticum, 119
Levisticum officinale, *119*
Light, artificial, 63, *64*
Ligusticum. See Levisticum
Lily, 16
Lime flowers, 84
Limestone, 29, 30, 32
Lincoln asparagus. *See Chenopodium bonus-henricus*
Linen cupboard sachets, 86
Lippia, 120
Lippia citriodora, *120*
Lippia triphylla, 120
Liquorice, 13, 23. *See also Glycyrrhiza glabra*
Lobelia, 70
Lotions, bath, 87
Lotions, herbal, 22
Lovage, 26, 76, *119*. *See also Levisticum officinale*
Lovage, cutting, 68
Lovage, drying, 71
Lovage, feeding, 36

Love potions, 17
Lungwort, 20, 22

M

Madder, 44
Mahuang, 13
Maintenance, routine, 39
Maître d'hotel butter, 78, 130
Majorana. See Origanum
Malathion, 59
Mallow, 27
Mallow, marsh, 57, *94*. *See also Althaea officinalis*
Mantle, lady's, *44*, *48-49*, *83*, *92*. *See also Alchemilla xanthochlora*
Manure, 32, 89
Marathon, 13
Marigold, *51*. *See also Calendula officinalis*
Marigold, marsh, *102*. *See also Caltha palustris*
Marigold, pot. *See Calendula officinalis*
Marinades, herb-flavoured, 78
Marjoram, 7, 9, 21, 30, 52, 56, 75, 76, 77, 84, 85. *See also Origanum*
Marjoram, disbudding, 68
Marjoram, drying, 70
Marjoram, harvesting, 69
Marjoram, hop. *See Origanum dictamnus*
Marjoram jelly, 84
Marjoram, knotted. *See Origanum majorana*
Marjoram, pot. *See Origanum onites*
Marjoram, sweet, *127*. *See also Origanum majorana*
Marjoram, wild. *See Origanum vulgare*
Marrubium, 120
Marrubium vulgare, 120
Marsh mallow, 57, *94*. *See also Althaea officinalis*
Marsh marigold, *102*. *See also Caltha palustris*
Marygolds, 22
Materia Medica, 16
Matricaria, 121
Matricaria chamomilla, 121
Matricaria eximia. See Chrysanthemum
May wine, 50
Mayonnaises, herb-flavoured, 78
Mayweed, scented. *See Matricaria chamomilla*
Meadow saffron, 107
Meadowsweet, *110*. *See also Filipendula vulgaris*
Meat seasonings, 84
Medicinal herbs, *6*, 8, 13, 16, 17, 21, 22
Medicines, folk, 20, 22
Melissa, 121
Melissa officinalis, *121*
Mentha, 122, 123
Mentha x piperita, *122*
Mentha pulegium, 122
Mentha rotundifolia, 122, *123*
Mentha spicata, 122, *123*
Menthol, 23
Mice repellents, 22
Milfoil. *See Achillea millefolium*
Miniature herb gardens, *28*
Mint, 7, 8, 11, 12, 16, 21, 23, 25, 26, 30, 31, *44*, 52, 58, 62, 63, 76, 84, 87. *See also Mentha*
Mint, apple, 11, 12, 30, *123*. *See also Mentha rotundifolia*
Mint, containing, 9
Mint, drying, 70, *71*
Mint jelly, 78
Mint, orange, 55, 85
Mint, round-leaved. *See Mentha rotundifolia*
Mint sauce, 7
Mint vinegar, 77, 80
Mint, woolly. *See Mentha rotundifolia*
Mites, red spider, 59
Mixtures, dried herb, 75
Mixtures, scented, 67
Monarda, 123
Monarda didyma, *123*
Monastery herb gardens, 12, 17
Moonlight gardens, 12, *14-15*
Morphia, 23
Moss peat. 28, 30, 33, 35, 36, 37, 39
Moth repellents, 22, 86
Motherwort, 52
Mould, 73
Mountain rue, 16
Mulches, 11, 36, 39
Mullein, *19*, 22, *44*, *148*. *See also Verbascum thapsus*
Muslin, 33, 74, 77, 85
Mustard, 9, 20, 36, *140*. *See also Sinapis alba*
Mustard, white. *See Sinapis alba*
Mustard, yellow. *See Sinapis alba*
Myrrhis, 124
Myrrhis odorata, 124
Myrtle, 17, 21, *42*, *43*, 82, *124*. *See also Myrtus communis*
Myrtus, 124
Myrtus communis, *124*

N

Nasal decongestants, 13
Nasturtium, 9, 56, 57, 67, 125, *146. See also Tropaeolum majus*
Nasturtium officinale, 125
Nepal cinquefoil, *44*
Nepeta, 125
Nepeta cataria, 125
Nettle, spotted dead, *117. See also Lamium maculatum*
Nitrogen, 28, 29
Nosegay, 16, 21, 22, 23, *82*
Nursery herbs, planting out, 34
Nursery plants, 9
Nutrients, 28, 33, 62

O

Ocimum, 126
Ocimum basilicum, 126
Oils, 23, 68, 75
Oils, aromatic, 10, 36
Ointments, 22, 23
Olive, sweet, 55, *128. See also Osmanthus fragrans*
Onion, Egyptian, 10, *92. See also Allium cepa var. viviparum*
Onion, salad, 9, 10, 27. *See also Allium*
Orach, 9, 12. *See also Atriplex hortensis*
Orange, calamondin, *106. See also Citrus microcarpa*
Orange mint, 55, 85
Oregano, *83, 127. See also Origanum vulgare*
Oregano butter, 78
Organic matters, 28, 29
Origanum, 127
Origanum dictamnus, 127
Origanum majorana, 127
Origanum onites, 127
Origanum vulgare, 127
Ornamental chives, *51, 83*
Orris, 57, 86, *115. See also Iris germanica var. florentina*
Osmanthus, 128
Osmanthus fragrans, 128
Oswego tea, 84. *See also Monarda didyma*
Our Lady's candle. *See Verbascum thapsus*
Oven drying, 71
Overwatering, 65

P

Palm, fan, 18, *19*
Pansy, 21. *See also Viola*
Pansy, wild. *See Viola tricolor*
Parkinson, John, 16, 20, 21
Parsley, 9, 13, 25, 27, 30, *46*, 55, 57, 76, 77, 78, 84, *131. See also Petroselinum crispum ssp. crispum*
Parsley, Chinese. *See Coriandrum sativum*
Parsley, cutting, 68, *69*
Parsley, dried, 75
Parsley, drying, 71
Parsley, freezing, 73, 74
Parsley, germination rate, 34
Parsley, Hamburg, *131. See also Petroselinum crispum ssp. tuberosum*
Parsley, indoor, 56
Parsley jelly, 78
Parsley, potting, 37
Parsley, sowing, 27
Parsley, turnip-rooted. *See Petroselinum crispum ssp. tuberosum*
Pastis, 23
Paths, 40, *44, 48, 50, 51*
Patterns, herb gardens, *10-11*, 40-53
Pearl everlasting, 22, *82*
Peas, cat's. *See Cytisus scoparius*
Peat, moss. *See Moss peat*
Peat pots, 34
Pebbles, 62, *63*
Pelargonium, 129
Pelargonium capitatum, 61
Pelargonium x *citrosum, 128*
Pelargonium crispum, 60, 129
Pelargonium denticulatum, 61
Pelargonium x *domesticum* 'Clorinda', *60, 129*
Pelargonium graveolens, 60, 61, 129
Pelargonium tomentosum, 61, 129, 130
Pelargoniums, scented, *60-61*
Penn, William, 52
Pennyroyal, 52, 70, *122. See also Mentha pulegium*
Pepper cress. *See Lepidium sativum*
Peppermint, 30, 70, *122. See also Mentha* x *piperita*
Peppermint-scented geranium, *54*, 55, *61, 130. See also Pelargonium tomentosum*
Perennial herbs, 10, 26, 29, 31
Perennial herbs, propagation, 36, 37
Perennial herbs, sowing, 34

Perfumes, 16, 17, 23
Perilla, 130
Perilla frutescens, 130
Perilla frutescens var. *crispa, 130*
Perilla, purple, *130. See also Perilla frutescens* var. *crispa*
Pest resistance, 8, 36
Pesticides, 59
Pestilence deterrents, 13
Pesto, 78, 84, 126
Pests, 57, 59
Pests, dealing with, 59
Petals, storing, 85
Petroselinum, 130
Petroselinum crispum ssp. *crispum, 130, 131*
Petroselinum crispum ssp. *tuberosum, 131*
Peucedanum. See Anethum
pH scale, 28, 29, 30, 89
Pharmacopoeia, 20
Phew plant. *See Valeriana officinalis*
Phosphorus, 29, 33
Pie, cherry. *See Heliotropium arborescens*
Pillows, herb, 85, 86
Pimpinella, 132
Pimpinella anisum, 132
Pinching back, 68
Pinching out, 39
Pine-needle mulches, 39
Pistou, 78, 84, 126
Plague, antidotes for, 13, 23
Plant associations, 27
Plant labels, *32*, 34
Planting, *11*
Planting distances, 10, 26
Planting holes, 35, 36, *58*
Planting out, 34
Planting seasons, 32
Plasters, herbal, 22
Plastic pots, 59
Pliny, 27
Plots, herb, 26, 27
Pomanders, 87
Pools, 40, *42*
Poppy, 23
Portulaca, 132
Portulaca oleracea, 132
Positions for herb gardens, 25
Posset, 22
Pot herbs, 50, 54-65
Pot marigold. *See Calendula officinalis*
Pot marjoram. *See Origanum onites*
Pot sizes, 62
Potassium, 29, 33
Potato, 18
Poterium. See Sanguisorba
Potions, 13
Potpourris, 7, 8, 10, *66*, 67, 85, 86
Pots, flower, 59
Pots, types of, 34, 59
Potted herbs, 56, 57
Potting compost, 38, 56, 58, 62, 89
Potting up, 38, 57, 62
Preparation, soil, 27, 28, 32
Preservation of herbs, 68-76, *79-83*
Primula, 133
Primula officinalis, 133
Primula veris, 133
Propagation, 89
Propagation, division, 35, 36
Propagation, indoor, 57
Propagation, layering, 38
Protection, winter, 39
Provins, rose of. *See Rosa gallica*
Pruning, 10, 12, 40, *42, 43*, 57, 62, *63*
Purple perilla, *130. See also Perilla frutescens* var. *crispa*
Purslane, *132. See also Portulaca oleracea*
Purslane, sea, *100. See also Atriplex hortensis*
Pyrethrum. See Chrysanthemum

R

Radish, 27
Railway sleepers, 31
Raised beds, 26, *30*, 31, 40, *44, 45*
Red orach, 9, 12. *See also Atriplex*
Red spider mites, 59
Remedial herbs, 13
Remembrance, rosemary, 17
Repotting, 57, 62, *63*
Restriction, root, 26, 51, 62
Retaining walls, 31, *48-49*
Rock garden herbs, 25
Rod, Aaron's. *See Verbascum thapsus*
Roman chamomile. *See Anthemis nobilis*
Root cuttings, 38, 57
Root damage, winter, 39
Root pruning, 62, *63*
Root restriction, 26, 51, 62
Rooting powder, hormone, 37, 38, 39
Rorippa. See Nasturtium
Rosa, 133-134

Rosa calendarum, 133
Rosa damascena, 133
Rosa gallica, 134
Rosa gallica var. *damascena, 133*
Rose, *66*, 84. *See also Rosa*
Rose of Castile. *See Rosa damascena*
Rose, damask, *133. See also Rosa damascena*
Rose, French, *134. See also Rosa gallica*
Rose petals, 8, 85
Rose, propagation, 38
Rose of Provins. *See Rosa gallica*
Rose-scented geranium, *60*, 84, 85, *129. See also Pelargonium graveolens*
Rose water, 12
Rosemary, 7, 8, 11, 16, 25, 27, 30, 35, *44, 46*, 51, 75, 76, 77, 82, 84, 85, 86, 87, *88, 134. See also Rosmarinus officinalis*
Rosemary, drying, 70
Rosemary, harvesting, 69
Rosemary, indoor, 56
Rosemary jelly, 78, *79*, 84
Rosemary, propagation, 37
Rosemary, winter care, 39
Roses, shrub, 10
Rosmarinus, 134
Rosmarinus officinalis, 134
Round-leaved mint. *See Mentha rotundifolia*
Rue, 9, 12, 16, 27, *52, 83*, 136. *See also Ruta graveolens*
Rue, mountain, 16
Rumex, 135
Rumex scutatus, 135
Russian tarragon, 9. *See also Artemisia*
Ruta, 136
Ruta graveolens, 136

S

St. Patrick's cabbage. *See Sempervivum tectorum*
Sachets, 8, 10, 12, 85, 86
Sacrificial herbs, 17
Safflower, *103. See also Carthamus tinctorius*
Saffron, 16
Saffron crocus, *107. See also Crocus sativus*
Saffron, false. *See Carthamus tinctorius*
Saffron, meadow, 107
Saffron thistle. *See Carthamus tinctorius*
Sage, 9, 10, 11, 12, *14, 15*, 16, 20, 22, 30, 35, *45, 48-49*, 51, 52, *54*, 75, 76, 78, 80, *82, 83*, 84, *88*, 136. *See also Salvia officinalis*
Sage, drying, 70, 71
Sage, garden. *See Salvia officinalis*
Sage, propagation, 38
Salad burnet. *See Sanguisorba minor*
Salad, corn, *147. See also Valerianella officinalis*
Salad dressings, 78
Salad herbs, 9, 67
Salad onion, 10
Salads, 22
Salt, fertilizer, 59
Salting herbs, 74
Salts, herb-flavoured, 84
Salves, 13, 22
Salvia, 136-137
Salvia officinalis, 136
Salvia sclarea, 136, 137
Samphire, *107. See Crithmum maritimum*
Sand, coarse, 37, 38, 39, 62
Sandy soils, 28
Sanguisorba, 137
Sanguisorba minor, 137
Santolina, 10, 14, 138
Santolina chamaecyparissus, 138
Santolina incana, 138
Santolina tomentosa, 138
Sarothamnus. See Cytisus
Sarsaparilla, 70
Satureja, 138
Satureja hortensis, 138
Satureja montana, 138, 139
Sauce, mint, 7
Sauces, herb-flavoured, 78
Savory, 27, *51*, 84. *See also Satureja*
Savory, division, 35
Savory, drying, 70
Savory, summer, 9, 22, *138. See also Satureja hortensis*
Savory, summer, disbudding, 39
Savory, summer, harvesting, 69
Savory, winter, *46*, 56, *139. See also Satureja montana*
Savory, winter, harvesting, 68
Savory, winter, sowing, 34
Sawdust mulches, 36
Scale insects, 59
Scent mixtures, 7
Scented geraniums, 11, *60-61, 66*, 78
See also Pelargonium
Scented herbs, 10, 13, *60-61*
Scented mayweed. *See Matricaria chamomilla*
Screen trays, 71, *74*
Sea fennel. *See Crithmum maritimum*

Sea purslane, *100. See also Atriplex hortensis*
Seasonings, 55, 75, 84
Seed-grown herbs, 9, 33
Seed heads, 72
Seed leaves, *32*
Seedlings, planting out, 34
Seedlings, transplanting, *32*, 34, 57
Seeds, collecting, 72
Seeds, drying, 72, *76*
Seeds, sowing indoors, 57
Seeds, sowing outdoors, 33
Self-seeding, 36, 68
Sempervivum, 139
Sempervivum tectorum, *139*
Semsem. *See Sesamum*
Sesame, 18, *140. See also Sesamum indicum*
Sesamum, 140
Sesamum indicum, *140*
Sesamum orientale, 140
Shade, herbs for, 25, 26, 50, 63
Shakers, 22, 69
Shallot, 10, 77, *92. See also Allium ascalonicum*
Shisho, 130
Shock, transplanting, 34
Shrub roses, 10
Signatures, Doctrine of, 20
Silica gel, 86
Silver gardens, 12, *14-15*
Simples, 22
Simples, Garden of, *18-19*
Sinapis, 140
Sinapis alba, *140*
Sites, suitable, 11, 25
Sium, *141*
Sium sisarum, 141
Sizes, indoor, 56
Skirret, *141. See also Sium sisarum*
Slipper, lady's. *See Cytisus scoparius*
Smock, lady's, *102. See also Cardamine pratensis*
Snake repellents, 22
Sneezewort, *83*
Soaps, herb, 87
Soil chemistry, 29
Soil preparation, 27, 28, 32
Soil requirements, 25, 26, 28
Soil testing, 29
Sorrel, 9, *44*, *135. See also Rumex scutatus*
Sowing, autumn, 34
Sowing depths, 33
Sowing seeds indoors, 34, 57
Sowing seeds outdoors, 33
Sowing, successional, 33
Spanish juice. *See Glycyrrhiza glabra*
Spearmint, 30, 70, *123. See also Mentha spicata*
Species, 89
Specimen plants, 10
Speedwell, *148. See also Veronica officinalis*
Sphagnum moss, 38
Spice balls, 87
Spider mites, red, 59
Spinach, French. *See Atriplex hortensis*
Spiraea. See Filipendula
Spotted dead nettle, *117. See also Lamium maculatum*
Spring division, *35*
Spring onion. *See Salad Onion and Allium*
Spring planting, 32
Stachys, 141
Stachys lanata, 141
Stachys officinalis, *141*
Stachys olympica, 141, *142*
Star flower. *See Borago officinalis*
Steeples, church. *See Agrimonia eupatoria*
Stem cuttings, 9, *37*, 38, 57
Stone covering, 11
Storage containers, 73
Storing herbs, 73
Straw mulches, 39
Strawberry, alpine. *See Fragaria vesca*
Strewing herbs, 16, 17, 21, 22
Successional sowings, 33
Succory. *See Cichorium intybus*
Sugar, black. *See Glycyrrhiza glabra*
Sugar flavourings, 84
Sulphate, aluminium, 29
Sulphate, iron, 29
Sulphur, ground, 29, 30, 32
Summer coleus. *See Perilla frutescens var. crispa*
Summer savory, 9, 22, *138. See also Satureja hortensis*

Summer savory, disbudding, 39
Sun requirements, 25, 55, 63
Sunflower, 18
Sweet balm. *See Melissa officinalis*
Sweet basil, *126. See also Ocimum basilicum*
Sweet bay, 13, *117. See also Laurus nobilis*
Sweet cicely, 9, *124. See also Myrrhis odorata*
Sweet flag, 21, 26, *90. See also Acorus calamus*
Sweet marjoram, 7, 9, 21, 30, 52, 56, 75, 76, 77, 84, 85, *127. See also Origanum majorana*
Sweet olive, 55, *128. See also Osmanthus fragrans*
Sweet violet, *149. See also Viola odorata*
Sweet woodruff, 8, 25, 26. *See also Galium odoratum*
Symphytum, 142
Symphytum officinale, *142*

T

Tahina, 140
Tanacetum, 142, 143
Tanacetum vulgare, 142, *143*
Tansy, 12, 22, 86, *143. See also Tanacetum vulgare*
Tansy, division, 35
Taraxacum, *143*
Taraxacum officinale, *143*
Tarragon, 9, 25, 26, 30, 35, *52*, 55, 76, 77, 85, 99. *See also Artemisia*
Tarragon butter, 78
Tarragon, division, 35
Tarragon, dried, 75
Tarragon, French. *See Artemisia dracunculus*
Tarragon jelly, 78, *79*
Tarragon, propagation, 36
Tarragon vinegar, 77
Tea jasmine. *See Jasminum officinale*
Tea, Oswego, 84. *See also Monarda didyma*
Teasel, 22, *83*, *110. See also Dipsacus sylvestris*
Teas, herbal, 12, 13, 22, 70, 84
Temperature requirements, 55, 64
Tests, soil, 29
Teucrium, 143
Teucrium chamaedrys, *143*
Theatrum Botanicum, 20
Therapy, medical, 13
Thinning, 33, 34
Thistle, saffron. *See Carthamus tinctorius*
Thoroughwort, 70
Thyme, 7, 9, 11, 12, 13, 16, 23, 25, 27, 30, *45*, *46*, *47*, *48-49*, 51, 52, *54*, 55, 56, 57, 76, 77, *82*, *83*, 84, 85, 86, 87, *88. See also Thymus*
Thyme butter, 78
Thyme, creeping. *See Thymus serpyllum*
Thyme, drying, 71
Thyme, garden. *See Thymus vulgaris*
Thyme jelly, 78, 84
Thyme, lemon, 10, 44, *144. See also Thymus x citriodorus*
Thyme, sowing, 33, 34
Thyme, wild, *144. See also Thymus serpyllum*
Thymol, 23
Thymus, 144-145
Thymus x citriodorus, *144*
Thymus serpyllum, *144*
Thymus vulgaris, *144*, *145*
Times, planting, 32
Tip cuttings, *37*, 38
Tisanes, 12, 13, 22, 70, 84
Topiary, *42*, *43*
Towers, herb, *58*
Transpiration, 59, 65
Transplanting cuttings, *37*, 38
Transplanting seedlings, *32*, 34
Trays, drying, 71, *74*
Trigonella, 145
Trigonella foenum-graecum, *145*
Tropaeolum, 146
Tropaeolum majus, *125*, *146*
True aloe. *See Aloe barbadensis*
True lavender. *See Lavandula angustifolia*
Turner, William, 17
Turnip-rooted parsley. *See Petroselinum crispum* ssp. *tuberosum*
Tussie mussie, 16, *82*
Tussilago, 146
Tussilago farfara, *146*

U

Ulmaria. See Filipendula

Urns, glazed, 62
Uses of herbs, 40, 75, 76

V

Valerian, 23, *147. See also Valeriana officinalis*
Valerian, division, 35
Valeriana, 147
Valeriana officinalis, *147*
Valerianella, 147
Valerianella locusta, *147*
Valerianella olitoria, *147*
Vegetable dyes, 12, 67
Ventilation, 64, 70
Verbascum, 148
Verbascum, propagation, 38
Verbascum thapsus, *148*
Verbena, 148
Verbena, lemon, 11, 12, 84, 85, *120. See also Lippia citriodora*
Verbena officinalis, 148
Verbena triphylla. See Lippia
Vermiculite, 37, 38, 62
Vermouth, 23
Veronica, 149
Veronica officinalis, *149*
Vervain, 21, *148. See also Verbena officinalis*
Victory garlands, 13
Vinegars, herb, 67, 77, *80-81*
Vinegars, types of, 70
Viola, *66*, 149
Viola odorata, *149*
Viola tricolor, *149*
Violet, 9, 85. *See also Viola*
Violet, florist's. *See Viola odorata*
Violet, sweet, *149. See also Viola odorata*
Vitex, *83*

W

Wall germander. *See Teucrium chamaedrys*
Walls, retaining, 31, *48-49*
Water, Hungary, 17
Water temperatures, 65
Watercress, *125. See also Nasturtium officinale*
Watering, 33, 34, 35, 36, 58, 59, 62, 65
Waterlogging, 59
Weeding, 33
Wheel herb gardens, *44*
White jasmine. *See Jasminum officinale*
White mustard, *140. See also Sinapis alba*
Whiteflies, 59
Wild artichoke. *See Cynara cardunculus*
Wild marjoram. *See Origanum vulgare*
Wild pansy. *See Viola tricolor*
Wild thyme, *144. See also Thymus serpyllum*
Window sill, aspect, 63
Window sill herbs, 7, 8, 34, *54-65*
Wine, May, 50
Winter care, 39
Winter protection, 39
Winter savory, *46*, 56, *139. See also Satureja montana*
Winter savory, division, 35
Winter savory, sowing, 34
Wintergreen, 22, 70
Wire mesh, *58*
Witches' potions, 13
Woad, 12, *44*, *115. See also Isatis tinctoria*
Wood ashes, 33
Wood betony, *141. See also Stachys officinalis*
Wood chips, *50*
Wood preservative, 30, 31
Woodruff, *50*, 62, 63, *112. See also Galium odoratum*
Woodruff jelly, 78, *79*
Woodruff, sweet, 8, 25, 26. *See also Galium odoratum*
Woolly betony. *See Stachys olympica*
Woolly mint. *See Mentha rotundifolia*
Wormwood, 12, 22, 23, 31, *47*, 86, 99. *See also Artemisia absinthium*
Wormwood, propagation, 37
Wort, bishop's. *See Stachys officinalis*
Woundwort. *See Stachys officinalis*
Wreaths, dried, 82, *83*

Y

Yarrow, 22, *44*, 51, 87, 90. *See also Achillea millefolium*
Yellow mustard. *See Sinapis alba*

Filmsetting by C. E. Dawkins (Typesetters) Ltd., London, SE1 1UN. ⊠
Printed and bound in Great Britain by Jarrold & Sons Ltd, Norwich